TEACH YOU

G000242240

MATHEMATICS

This book aims to help the reader working on his own to master the elementary principles of Mathematics. It is a guide round the simpler branches of Mathematics, an introduction through which the more specialised aspects of the subject can be approached. Rigorously scientific explanations are avoided as much as possible and only so much of the theory of the various rules is given as is absolutely necessary to a practical understanding of them. Numerous worked examples are included, and each chapter contains practice exercises, the answers to which are given at the back of the book. Metric (SI) units are used throughout.

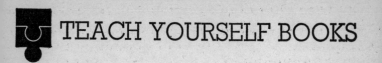
TEACH YOURSELF BOOKS

MATHEMATICS

Based on the work by
John Davidson, M.A.

Revised (1972) by
Harold Frayman

TEACH YOURSELF BOOKS
HODDER AND STOUGHTON

ST. PAUL'S HOUSE WARWICK LANE
LONDON EC4P 4AH

First printed 1938
Second edition 1965
Third edition 1970
Fourth edition 1972
Second impression 1974
Third impression 1975

Copyright © 1965, 1970, 1972
The English Universities Press Ltd

ISBN 0 340 16804 8

Printed in Great Britain
for Teach Yourself Books, Hodder & Stoughton
by Richard Clay (The Chaucer Press), Ltd.,
Bungay, Suffolk

Contents

Introduction

The title of this book, *Mathematics*, is perhaps a little
optimistic: the activities the word now covers are both
extensive and diverse. Certainly no one book can make
anything more than a slight dent in the total field of
mathematics.

The intention of this volume is to help the student who
wants to tackle mathematics for the first time and on his
own. It is a guide round the simpler branches of mathematics; it is an introduction through which the more
specialised aspects of mathematics can be approached.
Necessarily the pace is fast, especially early in the book,
so that you will have some sense of achievement as you
work through the text and exercises. But the advantage
of any book is that you can take it at your own speed.
If you reach the end of the book wanting and able to go
on to more difficult things, then this book will have suc-
ceeded and you will have forged some invaluable mathematical tools on the way.

The mathematics in this book is 'traditional' both in
form and in content: this is intentional. Especially if
you want mathematics as a practical aid, it is the most
direct approach involving the minimum of fuss. In the
text you are given the theory necessary for you to
understand the sample problems that are included: that
way your mathematical thinking will be more creative,
more likely to equip you to deal with unfamiliar
problems.

The exercises themselves are naturally artificial—they

have been invented for the book after all—but an attempt has always been made to resemble reality as much as possible. Often the answers to exercises 'work out', whereas this will rarely happen in practice; there is no merit in making problems complicated for complication's sake and the exercises are designed to test your grasp of the principles you have been trying to learn. To have arranged that the problems did not work out would have been to add fruitless confusion. On the other hand, you must not forget that genuine problems do not usually have tidy answers.

The answers to all the problems in this book are at the back. But a word of warning: please don't look answers up one by one or before you have reached some sort of answer. Working towards an answer you know is, in these circumstances, no test at all, since your having the right answer is the only assurance you can have that you have the correct method and theory.

This new edition has been revised to allow the introduction of one or two new topics. Decimals, particularly, have been brought into prominence, in response to the introduction of decimal currency and the proposed introduction of the metric system of measurement into Britain. The work in £p holds good for any decimal currency—and that takes in most of those in existence, as well as any future Euro-currency. The chapter on standard measures has been rewritten completely to provide a brief introduction to the metric system. For anyone who is completely unfamiliar with it, a preliminary glance at the chapter should prove rewarding.

For those problems which do not work out neatly, in this book or out of it, there is now an introduction to logarithms which will be very useful in complex calculations.

The book is divided by chapters, and, for the most part, chapters depend on preceding chapters; it is unwise to hop about too much, but some of the later chapters can be left out if you are not interested in their content. If, however, any chapter does not go far enough, then there will be an appropriate Teach Yourself Book designed to help you.

If the rudiments of mathematics are hard going, sometimes boring and often without any apparent practical value, nevertheless their mastery will repay amply. Only with them can the full excitement of mathematics be known, just as any other language cannot be exciting till you know how to form the sentences.

HAROLD FRAYMAN

CHAPTER I

A Basis

Mathematics is a complicated subject and the statements it makes are equally complicated. Statements in advanced mathematics may take up a line or two as they are normally written, but if they were to be translated into words—into standard English—they would run to many pages and be incredibly obscure. So that the obscurity can be kept to a minimum, mathematics develops its own language: this language is compact, a shorthand, and allows us to compress the complicated ideas which mathematics embraces in a readily comprehensible form. Much of this book is devoted to a development of this shorthand and of the basic theory which requires it. The mathematics is useful on its own, of course, but the real value of the work is to be found in the foundation which it provides for later work.

Necessarily a certain amount of mathematical knowledge, especially in arithmetic, is assumed. What follows immediately should be either revision or readily understandable.

Basic notation

Addition: The process of finding the sum of two or more numbers.

Symbol: **+** (read 'plus').

Subtraction: The process of finding the difference of two numbers.

Symbol: — (read 'minus').

Note: '10 − 7' means the amount by which 10 exceeds 7, and not vice versa; the order of the numbers matters.

Multiplication: The process of finding the sum of a given number of repetitions of a certain number. This 'repeated sum' is called the *product*.

Symbol: ✕ (read 'times' or 'multiplied by').

So, 5×6 is $6 + 6 + 6 + 6 + 6$ *or* $5 + 5 + 5 + 5 + 5 + 5$.

Division: The process of repeated subtraction until zero is reached: how many times is a number subtracted from another number so that the answer is zero?

Symbol: ÷ (read 'divide(d) by').

Note 1: Again the order of the numbers matters; $10 \div 2$ is not the same as $2 \div 10$.

Note 2: The solidus, or slash, /, is also used to denote division; e.g. $5/4 = 5 \div 4$; $-14/7 = -14 \div 7$.

Brackets: Symbols: **( ), { }, [ ]**.

Brackets are used to shorten statements in mathematics. If, for example, we wish to show that 5 and 7 are to be added and *then* subtracted from 18, we would show this by putting the $5 + 7$ in brackets, thus:

$$18 - (5 + 7).$$

A second example is obtained by considering:

$$(5 + 7) - \{5 - (2 + 1)\}.$$

This means that 2 and 1 are to be added first, then subtracted from 5, and the result subtracted from the sum of 5 and 7.

A fuller explanation of the use of brackets is in Chapter 6.

Operation: Any mathematical process by which two or more numbers are combined to give a new number.

Addition, subtraction, multiplication and division are all examples of operations.

Commutative operation: Any operation in which the order of the numbers to be combined does not matter, as with addition and multiplication. Operations where this is not so are called non-commutative—as, for example, subtraction and division.

Equality: The relation between two quantities which are identical in value.

Symbol: $=$ (read 'equals' or 'is equal to').

Note: the number of times the equality can be used in one expression is unlimited, so $2 = 1 + 1 = 4 - 2$, etc. Expressions which are not equal are inequal, for which the symbol is $\neq$. For example, $18 \div 3 \neq 3 \div 18$ (which is true because division is non-commutative). The symbol is read as 'is not equal to'.

Integer: Any whole number, including zero.

Positive: Greater than zero (of numbers).

Negative: Less than zero.

Factor: Any integer which, when multiplied by another integer, is equal to a particular number is a factor of that number.

Square: Any number which is the product of two equal numbers is a square. The square of a number is the product of that number multiplied by itself. So, 16 is the square of 4, 25 the square of 5 and so on. To indicate that a number is *squared* we put the figure 2 at the upper right-hand corner of the number, diminished in size, thus: $5^2 = 5 \times 5 = 25 = 5$ squared.

Cube: Any number which is the product of three equal

numbers. The cube of a number is the product of that number multiplied by itself twice. So, 64 is the cube of 4, 125 the cube of 5 and so on. To indicate that a number is *cubed* we put the figure 3 at the upper right-hand corner of the number, diminished in size, so $5^3 = 5 \times 5 \times 5 = 125 = 5$ cubed.

Square root (of a number): the number which, when squared, gives the required number. Thus 5 is the square root of 25.

Symbol: $\sqrt{}$ or $\sqrt{}$ (read 'root' or 'square root').

Note: $5 = \sqrt{25} = \sqrt{25} =$ root 25, since $5^2 = 25$.

Cube root of a number: the number which, when cubed, gives the required number. Thus 4 is the cube root of 64.

Symbol: $\sqrt[3]{}$ or $\sqrt[3]{}$ (read 'cube root').

Note: $4 = \sqrt[3]{64} = \sqrt[3]{64} =$ cube root 64, since $4^3 = 64$.

Therefore: Symbol: $\therefore$.

Because: Symbol: $\because$.

Is greater than: Symbol: $>$.

Is less than: Symbol: $<$.

These symbols and the simple concepts which are connected with them will be used often in the pages that follow. An adequate grasp of them is vital for progress.

EXERCISE I

1. Write out a longhand version of:

$10 + 10 + 10 + 10 + 10 = 5 \times 10 =$
$10 \times 5 = 100 \div 2 = 5^2 \times 2 = 10^2 \div 2$.

2. Add: (1) 35, 17, 21; (2) 341, 238, 1021; (3) 653, 475, 318.

3. Find: (1) $121 - 38$; (2) $192 - 64$; (3) 141 subtracted from 738.

4. Find the value of: (1) $38 + 72 - 41$; (2) $56 + 128 - 98$; (3) $348 + 836 - 947$.

5. Multiply: (1) 38 by 11; (2) 35 by 21; (3) 438 by 27.

6. Divide: (1) 836 by 11; (2) 3934 by 14; (3) 2072 by 37.

7. What is $38 \times 9 \times 7 \div 3 \div 2$?

8. What is: (1) the square of 6? (2) 7^2? (3) 2^3?

9. What is: (1) the square root of 81? (2) $\sqrt{64}$? (3) $\sqrt[3]{343}$?

10. Is it true that: (1) $47 > 36$? (2) $2814 < 3890$? (3) $-12 > -25$? (4) $56 > -56$?

Introduction to Algebra

So far we have only considered the arithmetical aspect of mathematics. The terms we have introduced apply to *all* aspects of mathematics. Let us consider a team of fifteen footballers whose total weight is 1485 kgf. To find the average weight of the footballers we must divide their total weight by the number in the team, and so we obtain the average weight, which is 99 kgf. We all know, almost instinctively, how to obtain this answer; but we need to be able to explain the method mathematically.

What did we do? We divided the total weight by the number of footballers: in other words, and using some mathematical shorthand,

$$the\ average\ weight = \frac{total\ weight}{number\ of\ footballers}.$$

We can abbreviate this still further by introducing some shorthand especially for this problem (as opposed to the shorthand we have introduced so far, which is universally applicable). Instead of writing *the average weight* let us, merely while solving the problem, write *a*; for *total weight* and *number of footballers* let us write *t* and *n* respectively. But all the time we will remember that *a*, *t* and *n* are only abbreviations. In practice we will read $a = \frac{t}{n}$ as '*a* equals *t* over *n*', but translated back from mathematical language it will continue to mean 'the average weight equals the total weight divided by the number of footballers'. The advantage of using shorthand should now be readily apparent.

The sentence, $a = \dfrac{t}{n}$, is a *general expression* of the method for finding the average weight of a team of footballers.

If at the beginning of the problem we had let x be the shorthand for average weight, y for total weight and z for the number of footballers, then we would have had

$$x = \frac{y}{z}$$

as our general expression. It does not matter what shorthand we decide upon, as long as we stick to it for the duration of the problem on hand, at least.

$a = \dfrac{t}{n}$ is actually a *definition* of the average weight: the value a, equal to t/n, is defined as the average weight. This differs from a mathematical law, such as Newton's Law that the forces acting on something are equal and opposite if the thing is to stand still.

Mathematical laws are not like human laws. If someone discovers a breach of human law, this will usually lead to a clampdown by the forces of law and order; it would be unusual for the law to be changed. However, when the law-makers feel that a law is no longer useful, they change it.

Not so with mathematical laws or physical laws. These laws do not prescribe behaviour, as human laws do, but rather describe it. If an exception to a mathematical or physical law can be found, then the law must be changed to allow for the exception.

Let us consider an example of a physical law. If a body is set in motion, the only reason why it should come to a stop is because it is acted upon by some force. For example, a ball set rolling along the ground only stops because the friction of the ground and of the air gradually stops it. Now, it has been proved that there is a fixed relation between the mass of the moving body, the force and the time during which the body is changing from one velocity to another. If the force be represented by F, the mass by m, the time by t, the first velocity by v_1 and the second velocity by v, then $F \times t = m \times (v_1 - v)$ or, in words, the force multiplied by the time = the product of the mass by the difference of the velocities.

The above form will be true whatever values F, t, m, v and v_1 may have. The moment we attach arithmetical numbers to the letters the result is true *only of those numbers*. But *as it stands* it is true of all problems involving force, time, mass and velocity. It is applicable to all; it is *general*, not particular. And it is *general* because the letters, unlike numbers 1, 4, 6, etc., stand for *any numbers whatsoever*. The form we call *algebraical*, as opposed to *arithmetical*. And it is evident that the form, or *formula*, as it is called, is a very convenient method of remembering scientific laws upon which so many practical problems depend. Thus all the experiments connected with projectiles depend upon the above and similar formulae. But there are numerous other relationships among natural objects that it is useful and necessary for many people to know, and which are conveniently expressed in *formulae*. Further, many an arithmetical problem can be more readily solved by algebraical methods than by arithmetical. The working out of these formulae, according to the various given values of the letters, must depend, as all calculation does, on the four fundamental operations of addition, subtraction, multiplication and division. Only, because *letters* are employed, as well as arithmetical numbers, to represent quantities, it may be expected that there will be some differences between arithmetical and algebraical operations. These differences, however, are more apparent than real; and if the student makes up his mind to see in algebraical operations only arithmetical processes *generalised*, he ought to find little difficulty.

Explanation of symbols

1. In Arithmetic 2, 5, 8, 10, etc., are definite numbers, that is, each has a *fixed* value.

In Algebra, a, b, c, d, x, y, z stand for *any values*.

In the same expression, however, such as $a + b - c + 2a - 3b$, the same letter is supposed to have the same value wherever it occurs.

Note: The letters a, b, c, etc., and the signs $+$, $-$, $\times$, etc., are called algebraic symbols, and any collection of algebraic symbols is called an *algebraic expression*. Thus $a + b - c$, $x - y + \sqrt{z}$, etc., are algebraic expressions.

The parts of an algebraic expression which are separated by the signs $+$ and $-$ are called the *terms* of the expression. Thus $a, + b, - c$ are the terms of the first expression above, and $x, -y, + \sqrt{z}$ are the terms of the second.

2. In Arithmetic and Algebra the sign $+$ has the same meaning, viz. to denote addition. Thus, in Arithmetic $2 + 4 = 6$; in Algebra $a + b$ means the sum of the quantities a and b.

In Algebra the sign $-$ is often used to denote that a larger quantity is subtracted from a lesser. Now, this can only be by employing the notion of a quantity *less* than 0, that is, a *negative quantity*. But this notion after all is not difficult to realise. Suppose that A possesses £100 and that B, instead of possessing any money at all, is in debt to the extent of £100. B's *wealth* cannot be represented by £0, but by —£100.

Again, suppose that a man starts from a certain point to walk along a road. Let AB in Fig. 1 represent the

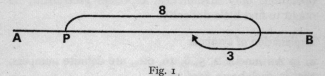

Fig. 1

road, P the starting-point and PB the direction in which the man walks. If he walks 8 km in the direction PB, then turns and walks 3 km back in the opposite direction, he will at the end of his walk be 8 — 3 or 5 km from P, this distance being measured in the direction PB. Denote this by +5. In general, if he walks a km in the

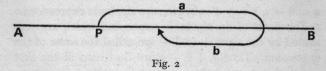

Fig. 2

direction PB and b km back (see Fig. 2), he will finally be $a - b$ km from P.

Suppose now that we take $a = 8$ and $b = 12$, then $a - b = 8 - 12 = -4$ (see Fig. 3). What, then, does this result mean? Can we give a meaning to it? Well, we

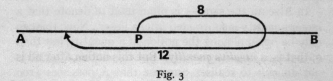

Fig. 3

know that if the man walks 8 km in the direction PB and 12 km back in the opposite direction, he will be 4 km on the opposite side of P. Hence −4 is interpreted as meaning 4 measured in a direction *opposite* to PB. In other words, if +4 denotes a distance of 4 km measured from P in the direction PB, −4 denotes a distance of 4 km measured from P in the opposite direction.

It is clear that we may choose either direction as the positive or + direction. Thus, if we take PA to be the positive direction, PB will be the negative (−) direction; and +4 will denote a distance measured in the direction PA, while −4 will denote a distance measured in the direction PB.

Again, take the measurement on the Centigrade (or Celsius) thermometer. On that thermometer the temperature at which water freezes is marked 0° (no degrees), and that at which water boils is marked 100° (100 degrees). But there are *lower* temperatures than 0° to which it is often necessary to refer, and these must be marked −. Thus +3°C or 3°C indicates 3 degrees *above* freezing-point, and −3°C indicates 3 degrees *below* freezing-point.

Hence:

3. A *sum*, or an addition, in Algebra may be the addition of *both positive and negative quantities*. For example, the sum of +a and −b is represented by the expression +a − b, or simply a − b. Then if a = 3 and b = 5, a − b would mean +3 − 5, or −2, or the *sum* of a positive 3 and a negative 5 is a negative 2.

4. In arithmetic 53 is a short way of representing 50 + 3, that is, 5 × 10 + 3, the 5 on account of its position representing not 5 units but 5 *tens*, that is, 5 × 10 units.

In Algebra such an expression as ab does not mean $10a + b$. The expressions ab, cd, xy, $3xy$, $6c$ all represent products. Thus $ab = a \times b$, $3xy = 3 \times x \times y$; a and b are the factors of ab, and 3, x, y are the factors of $3xy$.

In the product $3xy$, 3 is called the *numerical coefficient* of xy, and x and y the *literal* (or letter) coefficients of 3. If the quantities are complicated, their product is expressed by using *brackets*. For example, the product of $a + b$ and $c + d$ may be expressed as $(a + b) \times (c + d)$, or more usually $(a + b)(c + d)$.

5. If the same quantity is multiplied by itself several times, the product is expressed by writing the number of factors at the top right-hand corner of the quantity. Thus, the product $a \times a \times a \times a$ contains the factor a four times, and is therefore expressed as a^4—called a to the fourth *power*. Similarly, $x \times x \times x \times x \times x = x^5$, or x to the fifth *power*, and $2 \times 2 \times 2 \times 2 \times 2 \times 2 = 2^6$, or 2 to the sixth *power*.

The number expressing the power of any quantity is called its *index* or *exponent*. Thus, in a^2, 2^3, x^7, the little figures 2, 3, 7 are the *indices* of a^2, 2^3, x^7 respectively. When the index is unity we usually do not write a^1 but simply a.

Note: Distinguish between a *coefficient* and an *index*. Thus, there is a difference between $6a$ and a^6:

$$6a = a + a + a + a + a + a.$$
$$a^6 = a \times a \times a \times a \times a \times a.$$

6. If you are given that a number, x say, when raised to the power n gives y, then x is the nth root of y. So if $x^7 = y$, then $x = \sqrt[7]{y}$. This is a simple extension of the idea involved in a square or cube root.

Addition in algebra

Like terms

Example 1. Find the sum of $6x$, $3x$, $-10x$, $-3x$, $5x$, $-2x$. Here the positive $(+)$ terms amount to $14x$ $(6x + 3x + 5x)$; the negative (-1) terms amount to $15x$ $(10x + 3x + 2x)$. Thus the sum of the positive and negative terms is $+14x - 15x = -x$. Hence **the rule of addition**: Add all the positive terms, add all the negative terms, and find the difference between the two sums. This difference has the sign of the *greater* sum.

Unlike terms

Just as in arithmetic we cannot add different units except by keeping like quantities in the same column and unlike quantities in different columns, so in algebraical addition we place like terms in the same column and unlike terms in different columns. The necessity for this may be made quite evident from the following. The sum of £5 and 5p is neither £10 nor 10p but simply £5·05; so the sum of $2a$ and $2b$ is neither $4a$ nor $4b$ but simply $2a + 2b$.

Example 2. To find the sum of the quantities $2a$, $-b$, c, $-d$, $6a$, $3b$, $-2a$, $-3d$, we arrange the quantities as follows:

$$2a - b + c - d$$
$$6a + 3b$$
$$-2a \qquad\qquad - 3d$$

Then, sum $= \overline{6a + 2b + c - 4d}$.

Example 3. To find the sum of the quantities x^2, $-7x^2$, $9ab$, $4bc$, $-3x^2$, $6bc$, $-2ab$, $-xy$. The quantities are arranged as follows:

$$x^2 + 9ab + 4bc$$
$$- 7x^2 - 2ab + 6bc$$
$$- 3x^2 \qquad\qquad - xy$$

Then, sum $= -9x^2 + 7ab + 10bc - xy$.

Sometimes the expressions to be added consist of more than single terms, but the process of adding is the same as before.

Example 4. To find the sum of $a + 2b - c$, $6a - b$, $-a - b$, $7a - b$, $3a - b + c$, $5a + b - 2c$.

The arrangement is as follows:

$$a + 2b - c$$
$$6a - b$$
$$- a - b$$
$$7a - b$$
$$3a - b + c$$
$$5a + b - 2c$$

Then, sum $= 21a - b - 2c$.

EXERCISE 2

Add together:

1. a, $-5a$, $-7a$, $6a$, $10a$, $-3a$.
2. $4b$, $-10b$, $6b$, $-3b$, $-14b$.
3. x, $-2x$, $5x$, $7x$, $-8x$, $-9x$.
4. $2d$, $-3d$, $-4d$, $6d$, $-7d$.
5. x^2, $4x^2$, $-x^2$, $-9x^2$, $-7x^2$.
6. xy, $-6xy$, $5xy$, $-2xy$, $-7xy$.
7. x^2y, $-7x^2y$, $-2x^2y$, $-8x^2y$, $9x^2y$.
8. $2a - b - c$, $3a - 2b - c$, $5b + c + d$, $7a - 2b$, $9c$.
9. $8xy - 2b + y$, $9b - y$, $2xy + b + y$, $4xy - y - 3b$.
10. $a^2 - 2ab + b^2$, $3a^2 - ab - b^2$, $6ab + b^2$, $9a^2 - b^2$.
11. (a) $cx + cy - yz$, $\qquad 7cx - 2cy + 3yz$, $\qquad -8cx + 2cy$, $\qquad -3cx - 2cy - yz$.
    (b) Find the value of the result when $c = 1$, $x = 2$, $y = 3$, $z = 4$.

12. (a) $ax - 2bx - 6cx$, $3ax - cx$, $3bx + cx$, $-5ax + bx$, $2ax - bx - cx$.

   (b) Find the value of the result when $a = 2$, $b = 1$, $c = 3$, $x = 7$.

13. $\frac{2}{3}x + \frac{1}{4}xy - \frac{1}{5}y$, $\frac{1}{2}x - 2xy$, $-\frac{1}{3}y - \frac{1}{6}x$, $3x - \frac{1}{4}xy$.

14. $\frac{1}{2}a^3 - 2a^2b + \frac{3}{5}b^3$, $-\frac{1}{4}a^3 - a^2b$, $-a^2b - \frac{1}{2}b^3$.

15. $-2a - \frac{5}{2}c$, $6a + \frac{3}{2}c$, $5a - 2c$, $-6a - \frac{1}{3}c$, $9a + c$.

Subtraction in algebra

The following explanation may help you to understand the reason for the algebraic rule of subtraction.

Consider the following expressions:

$$(1) \ a + (b - c). \qquad (2) \ a - (b - c).$$

The first means that a is to be added to the difference of b and c, and this is the same thing as first to add b to a and then to subtract c. Hence $a + (b - c) = a + b - c$. That is, when $+$ precedes the bracket, the removal of the bracket does not affect the signs of the quantities inside the bracket.

Another way of looking at the expression is to think of the $+$ as adding to a every quantity within the brackets.

The second expression, $a - (b - c)$, means that $b - c$ is to be subtracted from a, or that *every quantity within the brackets is to be subtracted from a*. Now, the subtraction of b from a is represented by the expression $a - b$. What of the subtraction of $-c$ from a, that is, the subtraction of a *negative* quantity?

Fig. 4 shows the effect of a minus sign on a negative quantity.

Let AB be represented by a, and let the positive direction be from A to B (marked by the arrow). Suppose the length CB represents b, and CD represents c. Then $b - c$ is clearly the length represented by DB, so that $a - (b - c)$ is the length represented by AD. It is also clear, however, that AC represents $a - b$, so that AD also represents $(a - b) + c$, i.e. $a - b + c$. Therefore, $a - (b - c) = a - b + c$, since these expressions are both represented by AD. Hence the rule: If a minus

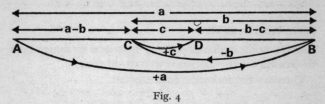

Fig. 4

sign precedes a bracketed expression, on the removal of the brackets each $+$ becomes $-$, and each $-$ becomes $+$; or, in other words, to subtract one quantity from another *change all the signs of the terms to be subtracted*.

Fig. 5 further illustrates the truth of the rule that

$$a - (b - c + d) = a - b + c - d,$$

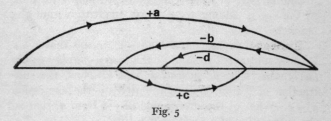

Fig. 5

where the positive quantity b becomes negative, the negative c becomes positive and the positive d becomes negative.

Sometimes the subtraction of a negative quantity is explained as follows. Suppose a man owes £10. If he is estimating his wealth, then, since the effect of the debt is to *diminish* his wealth by £10, he will denote his debt by -10. If, now, the debt be for some reason cancelled or taken away, that is, *subtracted*, the man will be richer by £10; and the result will be the same as if £10 had been added to his wealth; so that to *subtract* -10 is the same as to add $+10$. Thus, $+20 - (-10) = 20 + 10$.

Example 5. From $3a - 2b + c - 3d + e$ take $-2a + 6b - c - 2d - 5e$.

First method:

$3a - 2b + c - 3d + e - (-2a + 6b - c - 2d - 5e)$
$= 3a - 2b + c - 3d + e + 2a - 6b + c + 2d + 5e$
$= 5a - 8b + 2c - d + 6e.$

A second and more convenient method is to arrange the second expression under the first, as in arithmetic, *to think of the signs as changed* and then add, thus:

$$3a - 2b + c - 3d + e$$
$$-2a + 6b - c - 2d - 5e$$
$$\overline{5a - 8b + 2c - d + 6e}$$

Example 6.

From $\quad 5ax - 2by + 7xy - z$
Take $\quad 9ax + by - 3xy - 2z$
$$\overline{-4ax - 3by + 10xy + z}$$

EXERCISE 3

Subtract:

1. $3a - b + c$ from $-6a - b.$
2. $9x - y + z$ from $-3x + 2y - 2z.$
3. $8ab - 2xy$ from $-ab - xy + z.$
4. $x^2 - y^2$ from $-x^2 - y^2.$
5. $7xy + 2yz - 3xz$ from $-xy - xz.$

From:

6. $-p - q + r$ take $7p + q$.
7. $3p - 2q + r$ take $p - q - r + s$.
8. $ab + bc - cd$ take $-ab - cd$.
9. $pq + qr - s$ take $6pq - qr + 2s$.
10. $x^2 - y^2 - z^2$ take $9x^2 - 7y^2 - 3z^2$.
11. $\frac{1}{2}x^2 - y^2 - \frac{3}{4}z^2$ take $-x^2 - 2y^2 - \frac{1}{2}z^2$.
12. $\frac{1}{3}ab + 2bc - \frac{1}{4}cd$ take $-\frac{1}{4}ab - \frac{1}{2}bc$.

CHAPTER 3

Multiplication and Division in Algebra

Multiplication

1. $ab = a \times b$ or $b \times a$ or ba; this is the same as in arithmetic, where the product is the same no matter in what order the factors are taken. Multiplication is commutative.

2.
$$a^2 = a \times a = aa,$$
$$a^3 = a \times a \times a = aaa,$$
$$\therefore a^2 \times a^3 = aaaaa = a^5.$$

where the resulting index is the *sum* of the two indices.

3. $a(x + y) = a$ times each term inside the brackets
$$= a \text{ times } x + a \text{ times } y$$
$$= ax + ay.$$

Similarly,

$$(a + b)(c + d) = a \text{ times } (c + d) + b \text{ times } (c + d)$$
$$= ac + ad + bc + bd.$$

Compare the above operations with the following arithmetical operation:

$$
\begin{array}{r}
42 \\
36 \\
\hline
252 \\
1260 \\
\hline
1512 \\
\end{array}
$$

This operation may be represented as

$$
\begin{aligned}
(40 + 2)(30 + 6) &= 30 \text{ times } (40 + 2) + 6 \text{ times } (40 + 2) \\
&= 1200 + 60 + 240 + 12 \\
&= 1260 + 252 \\
&= 1512.
\end{aligned}
$$

From this it is evident that the multiplication process is really the same in both arithmetic and algebra.

4. Since $+$ and $-$ enter into algebraical operations, we shall meet in the course of multiplication with the following:

    (a) $+$ quantity $\times$ $+$ quantity gives what sign?
    (b) $+$,, $\times$ $-$,,   ,,   ,,
    (c) $-$,, $\times$ $+$,,   ,,   ,,
    (d) $-$,, $\times$ $-$,,   ,,   ,,

Consider $+$ and $-$ as representing, as before, *opposite directions*. Then:

    (a) $+5 \times +5$ must $= 5$ positive units taken 5 times in the positive direction, which $= +25$. Hence $+ \times + = +$.

    (b) $+5 \times -5$. Here 5 positive units taken 5 times gives $+25$, but taking account of the change of direction indicated by the $-$ sign, $+25$ becomes -25. Hence a positive quantity $\times$ a negative quantity $=$ a negative quantity.

    (c) $-5 \times +5$ is evidently the same thing as $+5 \times -5$.

    (d) -5×-5, as in (b), indicates that -5 is to be taken 5 times and the sign changed. But -5 taken 5 times $= -25$, and changing the sign we get $+25$. Hence $- \times - = +$.

Combining these results we have:

$$(1) \; \left. \begin{array}{l} + \times + \text{ gives} \\ - \times - \quad ,, \end{array} \right\} +.$$

$$(2) \; \left. \begin{array}{l} + \times - \quad ,, \\ - \times + \quad ,, \end{array} \right\} -.$$

Putting this into words, we have the *Rule of Signs* in multiplication:

(1) The product of two terms with *like* signs is *positive*.

(2) The product of two terms with *unlike* signs is *negative*.

Or, in an easily remembered form:

Like signs give +.
Unlike signs give −.

Example 1.

$$4ab^2 \times 2abc \left[\begin{array}{l} = 4 \times a \times b \times b \times 2 \times a \times b \times c \\ = 4 \times 2 \times a \times a \times b \times b \times b \times c \\ = 8 \times a^2 \times b^3 \times c \\ \quad = 8a^2b^3c. \end{array} \right.$$

The working in brackets is only explanatory. The product can be got at once.

Example 2.

$$3abc \times -2b^2c^3 \times -4a^2.$$

Here the signs of the first two quantities give −, and this sign, taken along with the − of the last quantity, gives +. Hence the product $= 24a^3b^3c^4$.

Example 3.

$$\begin{array}{l} a^2 - 2ab + b^2. \\ a - b \\ \hline a^3 - 2a^2b + ab^2 \\ - a^2b + 2ab^2 - b^3 \\ \hline a^3 - 3a^2b + 3ab^2 - b^3 \end{array}$$

In Example 3 we multiply the multiplicand by a, which gives $a^3 - 2a^2b + ab^2$; then we multiply it by $-b$, which gives $-a^2b + 2ab^2 - b^3$. When multiplying by $-b$, we take care to place like quantities in the same column, thus $2ab^2$ under ab^2, etc. Then we add just as in Arithmetic.

EXERCISE 4

Multiply:

1. abc by $2a^2b^2c^3$.
2. x^2y^2 by $-2x^2y^3x$.
3. $x + y$ by x^2.
4. $x^2 + 2xy + y^2$ by x^2.
5. $a + b + c$ by $a + b$.
6. $a^2 + 2ab + b^2$ by $a + b$.
7. $3x^2 - y^2$ by $x^2 + y$.
8. $a - b - c$ by $a^2 - b^2$.
9. $x + y$ by $x^2 - y^2$.
10. $-x^2 + y^2$ by $-x + y$.
11. $a^2 - 2ab + b^2$ by $a^2 + 2ab + b^2$.
12. $a - 2b + 1$ by $2a + b + 1$.
13. $\frac{1}{2}x^2 - \frac{1}{2}y^2$ by $\frac{1}{4}x^2 + \frac{1}{4}y^2$.
14. $\frac{1}{2}xy - \frac{1}{2}xz$ by $y^2 + z^2$.
15. $x^3 - y^3$ by $x^3 + y^3$.

Division

The process of algebraic division is exactly the same as in Arithmetic, as may be shown by the following:

$$16)542(33\tfrac{7}{8}$$
$$48$$
$$\overline{}$$
$$62$$
$$48$$
$$\overline{}$$
$$\tfrac{14}{16} = \tfrac{7}{8}.$$

This process in the extended form is:

$$16)500 + 40 + 2(31\tfrac{1}{4} + 2\tfrac{1}{2} + \tfrac{1}{8} = 33\tfrac{7}{8}$$
$$\underline{48}$$

$$20$$
$$\underline{16}$$

$$\tfrac{4}{16} = \tfrac{1}{4}$$
$$16)40(2$$
$$\underline{32}$$

$$\tfrac{8}{16} = \tfrac{1}{2}$$
$$2 \div 16 = \tfrac{2}{16} = \tfrac{1}{8}.$$

If the *Rule of Signs* is understood, there should be no difficulty about the signs in division. Since divisor × quotient = dividend, the sign of any term in the quotient will be *such a sign as when multiplied by the sign of the first term of the divisor will give the sign of the first term of the dividend*. Thus, if the divisor is $-x$ and the dividend $-xy$, the sign of the quotient is $+$, which along with the sign of the divisor gives $-$. Thus:

(1) $$-x)-xy(+y$$
$$-xy$$
$$\overline{}$$
$$..$$
$$\overline{}$$

(2) $$+x)-xy(-y$$
$$-xy$$
$$\overline{}$$
$$..$$
$$\overline{}$$

The rule of signs in division is thus seen to be the same as in multiplication, viz.:

Like signs (in divisor and dividend) give $+$ (in the quotient).

Unlike signs (in divisor and dividend) give $-$ (in the quotient).

Example 4.

$$x \overline{)x^2 - 2xy + 3x}$$
$$\overline{x - 2y\ + 3}$$

When the divisor consists of more than one term we proceed, as in Arithmetic, by considering how the *first* part of the divisor goes into the first part of the dividend.

Example 5.

$$x - y \overline{)x^2 - 2xy + y^2}(x - y$$
$$\underline{x^2 - xy}$$
$$- xy + y^2$$
$$\underline{- xy + y^2}$$

Here the result of dividing x^2 by x is x. We then multiply the whole divisor $x - y$ by this quotient x, which gives $x^2 - xy$. We then subtract this and take down the next part of the dividend. Next, the result of dividing $-xy$ by x is $-y$. We then multiply the whole divisor $x - y$ by $-y$ and subtract as before. And so on until there is no remainder. If there is a remainder, notice how we proceed:

$$a - b \overline{)a^2 - 2ab + 2b^2}\left(a - b + \frac{b^2}{a - b}\right.$$
$$\underline{a^2 -\ \ ab}$$
$$-\ \ ab + 2b^2$$
$$\underline{-\ \ ab +\ \ b^2}$$
$$b^2$$

Here the remainder is b^2, which is not exactly divisible by $a - b$. The division of b^2 by $a - b$ can only be represented by the fraction $\dfrac{b^2}{a - b}$. Now, this fraction must be *added* to the quotient. It would not do to put $b\dfrac{b^2}{a - b}$; for, while $3\frac{1}{2}$ means $3 + \frac{1}{2}$, in Algebra $b\dfrac{b^2}{a - b} = b \times \dfrac{b^2}{a - b}$, and so we must express the answer as above.

EXERCISE 5

Divide:

1. $3a^2$ by a.
2. $4ab$ by $-a$.
3. $8xyz$ by $-2y$.
4. $a^2 - b^2$ by $a - b$.
5. $a^2 + 2ab + b^2$ by $a + b$.
6. $a^2 - 2ab + b^2$ by $a - b$.
7. $a^3 - b^3$ by $a - b$.
8. $a^3 + b^3$ by $a + b$.
9. $a^2 - 2ab + 3b^2$ by $a - b$.
10. $a^3 - 4a^2x + 4ax^2 - x^3$ by $a - x$.
11. $2x^3 - 5x^2y - 9y^3$ by $x - 3y$.
12. $x^6 - a^6$ by $x^2 - ax + a^2$.
13. $x^4 - a^4$ by $x^2 + a^2$.
14. $x^3 - 3x^2y + 3xy^2 - y^3$ by $x - y$.
15. $p^4 - 4p^3q + 6p^2q^2 - 4pq^3 + q^4$ by $p - q$.

CHAPTER 4

Factors and Multiples—Highest Common Factor—Lowest Common Multiple

Before continuing, we shall have to consider the meaning of two words and the operations connected with them. The words are **factor** and **multiple**.

Factors

2 cm is contained in 8 cm four times exactly. 2, then, is said to be a measure or *factor* of 8. Similarly, it is a factor of 4, 6, 10, 12, 14, and so is called a *common factor* of these numbers. Since it is the highest number that is contained exactly in each of the above numbers, it is called their *highest common factor* (H.C.F.).

Multiples

Since the 8 cm above contains the 2 cm an exact number of times, the 8 cm is said to be a *multiple* of the 2 cm. Since 8 contains 2 and 4 exactly, 8 is said to be a *common multiple* of 2 and 4. And since 4 is the lowest number that contains 2 and 4 exactly, 4 is said to be the *lowest common multiple* (L.C.M.) of 4 and 2. Or, again, 15 is said to be the *lowest common multiple* of 5 and 3.

Summing up:

A factor is a number that divides another number exactly.

A common factor is a number that divides each of two or more numbers exactly.

The highest common factor is the highest number that divides each of two or more numbers exactly.

A multiple is a number that contains another number an exact number of times.

A common multiple is a number that contains each of two or more numbers exactly.

The lowest common multiple is the smallest number that is exactly divisible by each of two or more given numbers.

The object of finding the H.C.F. and the L.C.M. of two or more numbers is principally to facilitate our work with fractions. Here, however, are types of problems that illustrate a practical use of the ideas of H.C.F. and L.C.M.:

Example 1. Two vessels contain respectively 575 and 840 litres of liquid; find the vessel of greatest capacity that will completely empty both vats by an exact number of fillings.

Here 5 is the largest number that measures each of the numbers 575 and 840 exactly. Therefore, a 5-litre vessel is the largest that can be used to empty both if none of the liquid is to be left after the last complete vessel-ful.

Example 2. The sides of a triangular piece of ground measure 1640, 1592 and 1718 m respectively; find the length of the longest hurdle that can be used to fence it without bending or cutting a hurdle.

Here 2 is the largest number that divides each of the

three numbers exactly and so a 2-m hurdle is the longest
that can be used.

Example 3. A clock is wound up every 6 days, another
every 15 days. They are wound up together; how long
will it be before this happens again?

Here we want to find the lowest number of days that
will contain both 6 and 15 an exact number of times,
and this is evidently the L.C.M.: 30 days.

Example 4. The circumference of two cylinders is
4 cm and 5 cm respectively. What is the smallest length
of wire that can be wrapped round each an exact number
of times?

Evidently 20 cm of wire is the shortest length that
will contain 4 cm and 5 cm exactly.

But most of the 'problems' on H.C.F. and L.C.M. set
in text-books are somewhat fanciful and only apparently
practical; and one real utility, as we have said, of knowing
how to find the H.C.F. and L.C.M. of numbers is to
facilitate fractional operations. Accordingly, we proceed
to show how to find the H.C.F. and L.C.M. of two or
more numbers.

Highest common factor

Example 5. Suppose we wish to find the H.C.F. of 15,
20, 35. Break up each of the numbers into its simplest
factors, that is factors that cannot be broken up into
other factors, thus:

$$15 = 5 \times 3,$$
$$20 = 5 \times 2 \times 2,$$
$$35 = 5 \times 7.$$

From this it is apparent that 5 is the only measure that is found in each, it being found in 15 3 times, in 20 2 × 2 times, i.e. 4 times, and in 35 7 times. Hence 5 is the H.C.F. of 15, 20, 35.

Example 6.

$$60 = 5 \times 2 \times 2 \times 3,$$
$$75 = 5 \times 5 \times 3,$$
$$90 = 5 \times 3 \times 3 \times 2.$$

Here 5 occurs once and 3 occurs once in each of the numbers, hence the H.C.F. must be 5 × 3 or 15.

Now in ordinary life you rarely meet with fractional work that will necessitate your finding the H.C.F. of large numbers, and hence you may rest assured that the above method will enable you to find in an intelligent way an H.C.F. whenever required.

EXERCISE 6

1. Find the H.C.F. of 8, 10, 12, 16.
2.   ,,   ,,   15, 25, 75, 85.
3.   ,,   ,,   36, 42, 56, 68.
4.   ,,   ,,   12, 34, 48, 60.
5.   ,,   ,,   51, 102, 204, 306.
6.   ,,   ,,   37, 74, 148, 296.

Lowest common multiple

Example 7. To find the L.C.M. of two or more numbers.

As in the case of the H.C.F., break up the numbers into their simplest factors. Since the lowest number that contains each of the numbers must contain *all the factors of those numbers*, the L.C.M. will be readily seen by breaking up the numbers into their simplest or lowest factors. Thus:

$$8 = 2 \times 2 \times 2,$$
$$10 = 2 \times 5,$$
$$24 = 2 \times 2 \times 2 \times 3.$$

The L.C.M. must, therefore, contain $2 \times 2 \times 2$, otherwise it would not contain 8 or 24, each of which contains 2 3 times. It must also contain 5, for 5 is found in 10; and 3, for 3 is found in 24. Hence the L.C.M. must be $2 \times 2 \times 2 \times 5 \times 3$, or 120.

Example 8.

$$15 = 5 \times 3,$$
$$25 = 5 \times 5,$$
$$66 = 11 \times 3 \times 2;$$
$$\therefore \text{L.C.M.} = 5 \times 5 \times 3 \times 11 \times 2,$$
$$= 1650.$$

A short method of finding the factors is as follows:

$$\begin{array}{r} 3\overline{)15,\ 25,\ 66} \\ 5\overline{)5,\ 25,\ 22} \\ 1,\ \ 5,\ 22 \end{array}$$
$$\therefore \text{L.C.M.} = 3 \times 5 \times 5 \times 22$$
$$= 1650, \text{ as above.}$$

In this method we choose convenient factors, 3 and 5, and divide them in turn into any of the given numbers which are multiples, leaving non-multiples unchanged. This process may cease as soon as we have left a series of numbers with no common factors, as 1, 5, 22 in the example. The L.C.M. is then found by multiplying the factors and these remaining numbers together.

Exercise 7

1. Find the L.C.M. of 3, 4, 5, 6.
2.   ,,   ,,   7, 9, 10, 12.
3.   ,,   ,,   8, 12, 16, 18.
4.   ,,   ,,   12, 15, 18, 21.
5.   ,,   ,,   13, 39, 78.
6.   ,,   ,,   24, 56, 128, 39.

Methods of Shortening Multiplication and Division

Multiplication and Division occur so often in all our calculations that one is glad to shorten the work by any device possible. This chapter contains one or two simple techniques; for the solution to more difficult problems, see Chapter 12.

Multiplication by factors

This method may be explained thus: 114×28 means 114 taken 28 times, or 28 groups of 114. Now, since $28 = 7 \times 4$ (where 7 and 4 are *factors* of 28), the number in 28 *groups of* 114 = the number in 4 *groups of* 114 *taken 7 times*, or the number in 7 *groups of* 114 *taken 4 times*.

Hence $114 \times 28 =$ (1) $(114 \times 7) \times 4$, or

(2) $(114 \times 4) \times 7$.

(1) $= 798 \times 4$

$= 3192$.

(2) $= 456 \times 7$

$= 3192$.

In actual practice all that would be put down would be 798, 3192; 456, 3192. By this method we always save ourselves the *addition* operation of the ordinary method.

Thus, ordinary method:

$$\begin{array}{r} 912 \\ 228 \\ \hline 3192 \end{array}$$

Division by factors

The method may be explained thus: 5376 marbles ÷ 48 marbles means that we are to find how many groups of 48 there are in 5376. Now, 48 = 6 × 8. Therefore, if we first divide 5376 by 8, we shall get the number of *groups* containing 8 marbles. Then, if we divide this *number of groups* (of 8) by 6, we shall have a certain number of *groups of* 6, each containing 8 marbles; that is, *groups of* 48.

Example 1. 10 368 ÷ 72.

> 9)10 368
>   8)1 152 groups of 9
>   144 groups of (8 groups of 9);
>
>   that is, 144 groups of 72.

Notice how remainders are treated.

Example 2. 8 573 921 ÷ 63.

> 9)8 573 921
> 7)952 657 groups of 9, and 8 units over
>   136 093 groups of (7 containing 9 units each),
>   and 6 groups of 9 over.

6 groups of 9 = 54, and this added to the previous remainder of 8 units makes 62 units altogether.

Hence the rule: if there is a remainder after dividing by the second factor, *multiply this remainder by the first factor, and add to it the remainder (if any) after the division by the first factor.*

Example 3. 7 423 979 ÷ 84.

> 12)7 423 979
>   7)618 664 and 11 over
>   88 380 and 4 over.

Thus the remainder is $(4 \times 12) + 11$, or 59.

Multiplication by any one of the numbers from 11 to 19

The following short method should be known and used by the student. For example:

$$45\,672 \times 17.$$

First consider the ordinary method:

$$
\begin{array}{r}
45\,672 \\
17 \\
\hline
319\,704 \\
456\,72 \\
\hline
776\,424
\end{array}
$$

In this example it will be noticed that the second item in the final addition is 456 72 (short for 456 720), the same as the original multiplicand. Thus the multiplication by 7 and the addition may both be included in the following mental process:

7 times 2 = 14; 4 and carry 1.

7　,,　7 = 49, and 1 carried = 50, and 2 = 52; 2 and carry 5.

7　,,　6 = 42, and 5 carried = 47, and 7 = 54; 4 and carry 5.

7　,,　5 = 35, and 5 carried = 40, and 6 = 46; 6 and carry 4.

7　,,　4 = 28, and 4 carried = 32, and 5 = 37; 7 and carry 3.

3 and 4 are 7.

The multiplication is therefore performed in a single line.

Example 4.

$$845\,679$$
$$18$$

$$\overline{15\,222\,222}$$

Reduced mental process:

Eight 9's 72
,,   7's 56, 63, 72
,,   6's 48, 55, 62
,,   5's 40, 46, 52 $\Big\} = 15\,222\,222.$
,,   4's 32, 37, 42
,,   8's 64, 68, 72
    8 and 7 15

Multiplication by algebraic means

1. It will be easily seen, since $9 = 10 - 1$, that $9x = 10x - 1x$, where x represents any number. Thus

$$9 \times 38 = 10 \times 38 - 1 \times 38 = 380 - 38 = 342.$$

The same method can be used for multiplication of any number by raising it to the next multiple of 10 or 100.

Note that $8 = 10 - 2$ and $8x = 10x - 2x$,
$$97 = 100 - 3 \text{ and } 97x = 100x - 3x,$$

and also $198 = 200 - 2$ and $198x = 200x - 2x$.

Example 5. Multiply 129 by 293

$$129 \times 293 = 300 \times 129 - 7 \times 129$$
$$= 38\,700 - 903$$
$$= 37\,797.$$

2. We have shown earlier that

$$(a - b)(c - d) = ac + bd - bc - ad.$$

This can be used in ordinary multiplications as follows:

Example 6. Multiply 129 by 293.

$$\text{Now } 129 = 130 - 1$$
$$293 = 300 - 7.$$

Let $a = 130$, $b = 1$, $c = 300$ and $d = 7$.
Then $129 \times 293 = (130 - 1)(300 - 7)$
$$= 130 \times 300 + 1 \times 7 - 1 \times 300 - 130 \times 7$$
$$= 39\,000 + 7 - 300 - 910$$
$$= 39\,007 - 1210$$
$$= 37\,797.$$

The reader should compare this solution with Example 5.

Multiplication and division by 10, 100, 1000, etc.; 25, 75, 125

To multiply any number by 10 simply add 0, or a 'nought', to the right hand; to multiply by 100 add two 'noughts'; to multiply by 1000 add three 'noughts'; and so on. Thus, $415 \times 10 = 4150$, $415 \times 100 = 41\,500$, etc.

To divide any number by 10 cut off the figure farthest to the right; this will be the remainder. Thus, $415 \div 10 = 41$ and 5 over.

To divide by 100 cut off the two figures farthest to the right and so on.

Example 7.

$$8762 \div 100 = 87 \text{ and } 62 \text{ over.}$$
$$8762 \div 1000 = 8 \text{ and } 762 \text{ over.}$$

This will receive further explanation when we come to deal with decimals.

Since $25 = 100 \div 4$, we can multiply a number by 25 by adding two 'noughts' to the number and dividing by 4. Thus:

$$87\,432 \times 25$$
$$4)\overline{8\,743\,200}$$
$$2\,185\,800$$

Since $75 = 3 \times 25$, to multiply by 75 we can first multiply by 25 as above and then multiply the result by 3.

Since $125 = 1000 \div 8$, to multiply by 125 we add three 'noughts' to the number and divide by 8. Thus:

$$752\,398 \times 125$$
$$8)\overline{752\,398\,000}$$
$$94\,049\,750$$

The corresponding divisions by 25, 75 and 125 must be left alone at this point, as they involve difficulties which have to be explained later on.

The above are only a few examples of what can be done to lighten the load of calculation. The student is advised to study carefully the worked examples throughout this book, where he will meet with further illustrations of short processes, and to look out for and practise short methods himself.

Exercise 8

1. If one factor of a number is 11 and the other factor is 4, what is the number?
2. If one factor of a number is 12 and the other factor 7, what is the number?
3. If one factor of 39 is 3, what is the other factor?
4. If 75 is a product of two factors, one of which is 3, what is the other factor?
5. If 128 is the dividend and 4 the divisor, what is the quotient?
6. If 84 is the divisor and 3 the quotient, what is the dividend?

7. If the dividend is 876 and the quotient is 4, find the divisor.

8. If the divisor is 4, quotient 9, and remainder 2, what is the dividend?

9. If 5 × A = 30, what is the value of A?

10. If 16 × P = 48, what is the value of P?

11. If 36 = 6 × P, what is the value of P?

12. If 84 = P × 3, what is the value of P?

Multiply, by the method of *factors*:

13. 17 895 by 16, 35, 49, 72.

14. 318 246 by 15, 63, 108.

Multiply:

15. 942 793 by 10, 100, 1000, 10 000.

16. 7423 by 13, 14, 15, 16, 17, 18, 19.

17. 89 579 by 25, 75, 125.

Divide by the method of *factors*:

18. 18 456 by 15, 18, 24, 72.

19. 94 273 by 16, 22, 27, 108.

20. Divide 98 456 by 10, 100, 1000, 10 000.

CHAPTER 6

The Use of Brackets

Suppose we want to express the difference between a and the sum of b and c. We may do so by the following:

$$a - (b + c) \text{ or } (b + c) - a.$$

Now, suppose we wish to express the difference between these two expressions. We do so by the following form:

$$\{a - (b + c)\} - \{(b + c) - a\}.$$

The first expression $= a - b - c$ (according to the rule of signs in subtraction). The second expression $= b + c - a$. The difference between the two may then be expressed as $(a - b - c) - (b + c - a)$, and this form in turn becomes, by the rule of signs, $a - b - c$ $b - c + a$, which $= 2a - 2b - 2c$.

In simplifying such expressions it is convenient to begin with the innermost brackets. The following is a more complicated example:

$$b - [a - 2\{b - (c + d) - (2a - b)\} - 3a - b]$$
$$= b - [a - 2\{b - c - d - 2a + b\} - 3a - b]$$
$$= b - [a - 2b + 2c + 2d + 4a - 2b - 3a - b]$$
$$= b - a + 2b - 2c - 2d - 4a + 2b + 3a + b$$
$$= -5a + 3a + 6b - 2c - 2d$$
$$= -2a + 6b - 2c - 2d.$$

Consider this last result; 2 is evidently a factor of each term, and we can therefore express the result in the following form:

$$2(-a + 3b - c - d),$$

where the bracket shows that each term inside is to be multiplied by 2.

But if we put the minus sign *outside* the bracket, then we must *change each sign inside the bracket*, otherwise the original expression would be altered in value. Thus, suppose we put the expression into the form

$$-2(a + 3b - c - d);$$

this, when the bracket is removed, becomes

$$-2a - 6b + 2c + 2d,$$

which is different from the original expression. The correct expression must be

$$-2(a - 3b + c + d).$$

Next, suppose we want to group the four terms in two, taking the first two as the first term and the second two as the second term. We do so as follows:

$$-2(a - 3b) - 2(c + d).$$

The proof that we have not altered the *value* of the original expression may be had by removing the brackets, that is, by multiplying -2 into each term of the first bracket and -2 into each term of the second bracket, thus:

$$-2 \times a = -2a; \; -2 \times -3b = +6b;$$
$$-2 \times c = -2c \; -2 \times +d = -2d.$$

From what has been already said it can be seen that the terms of an expression can be combined and bracketed in any way, provided we *change the signs* inside a bracket *when it is preceded by a minus sign*. When it is preceded by a plus sign there is no change.

Example 1. Bracket the terms of the following expression in pairs:

$$3a - 9b + c - d - 2a + 6d$$
$$= (3a - 9b) + (c - d) - (2a - 6d),$$
$$\text{or } 3(a - 3b) + (c - d) - 2(a - 3d).$$

EXERCISE 9

Simplify:

1. $(a + b) - (c + d)$.
2. $2(a - b) - 3(c - d)$.
3. $-(a - b) - (c - d)$.
4. $-2(a - b) + (c - d)$.
5. $a - \{a - (b + c) - 2a\}$.
6. $x - (\frac{1}{2}x + \frac{1}{5}x + \frac{1}{10}x)$.
7. $p - \{q - (r + s - p)\}$.
8. $x - [y - (z + x) - \{2x - (y + z)\}]$.
9. $2p - 2[q - \{r - (s + p)\} - 3q]$.
10. $2\{ab - (cd - ef) - 2(ab - cd)\}$.

Bracket the terms of the following expressions in pairs:

11. $-p - q - r + s$.
12. $2p - q + r - s$.
13. $-xy - yz - p - 2q + r - s$.
14. $6ab - 2bc - 3cd - 4de - 5ef + 6fg$.
15. $-p + q + 2r - s - t + w$.
16. $-2p - 4q - r + s - 2t - 2w$.

CHAPTER 7

Evaluating Algebraic Expressions

Examples of how to evaluate algebraic expressions.

Example 1. Given $a = 5$, $b = 4$, $c = 3$, $d = 1$, find the value of $6a + 2b - (c^2 + 2d)$.

The given expression
$$= 30 + 8 - (9 + 2)$$
$$= 38 - 11$$
$$= 27.$$

Example 2. If $a = 7$, $b = 9$, $c = 2$, $d = 0$, find the value of $3a^2 + 2bcd - 3c^2$.

The given expression
$$= (3 \times 49) + (2 \times 9 \times 2 \times 0) - (3 \times 4)$$
$$= 147 + 0 - 12$$
$$= 135.$$

Example 3. If $V = 6$, $t = 15$, $g = 32$, find the value of S where $S = Vt + \frac{1}{2}gt^2$.

$$S = (6 \times 15) + \left(\frac{1}{2} \times \overset{16}{32} \times 15^2 \right)$$

$$= 90 + (16 \times 225)$$
$$= 90 + 3600$$
$$= 3690.$$

EXERCISE 10

If $a = 6$, $b = 4$, $c = 10$, $d = 5$, $e = 7$, $f = 12$, $g = 0$, find the values of:

1. $3ab + 2bc - c^2 - de$.

2. $a^2 + b^2 - c + de$.

3. $6(a - b) + 3c^2 - (d + e) - fg$.

4. $2b^2 + 3d - abc + e^2$.

5. $\dfrac{a + b + c}{2d}$.

6. $\dfrac{abc + bcd}{6(a + b)}$.

If $V = 5$, $t = 20$, $g = 32$, find the values of S in the following forms:

7. $S = \dfrac{V^2}{2g}$.

8. $S = Vt - \frac{1}{2}gt^2$.

9. If $W = 70$, $V = 120$, and $g = 32$, find the value of $\dfrac{WV^2}{2g}$.

10. If $W = 50\frac{1}{2}$, $V = 86$, and $g = 32$, find the value of $\dfrac{WV^2}{2g}$.

Examples of expressions containing square and other roots.

Example 4. If $a = 8$, $b = 9$, $c = 16$, $d = 8$, $e = 64$, find the value of $\dfrac{3\sqrt{bc} + \sqrt[3]{de}}{2\sqrt[3]{a} - \sqrt[4]{c} + \sqrt[6]{e}}$.

The expression

$$= \frac{3\sqrt{9 \times 16} + \sqrt[3]{8 \times 64}}{2\sqrt[3]{8} - \sqrt[4]{16} + \sqrt[6]{64}}$$

$$= \frac{(3 \times 3 \times 4) + (2 \times 4)}{(2 \times 2) - 2 + 2}$$

$$= \frac{36 + 8}{4}$$

$$= \frac{44}{4} = 11.$$

Example 5. If $a = 4$, $b = 1$, $c = 3$, $d = 9$, $e = 16$, $f = 32$, find the value of $\sqrt[3]{\dfrac{cd}{4\sqrt[4]{e}}} \div \sqrt{\dfrac{ad}{a^3b}}$.

The expression

$$= \sqrt{\frac{27}{4 \times 2}} \div \sqrt{\frac{4 \times 9}{64 \times 1}}$$

$$= \frac{3}{2} \div \frac{6}{8}$$

$$= \frac{3}{2} \times \frac{\overset{4}{8}}{\underset{2}{6}}$$

$$= 2.$$

EXERCISE 11

If $a = 16$, $b = 8$, $c = 3$, $d = 1$, $e = 0$, find the value of:

1. $3\sqrt{a} - 2\sqrt[3]{\dfrac{b}{4a}} + 5c^2\sqrt[4]{\dfrac{a}{d}}.$

2. $3\sqrt[3]{b} + 2c^2\sqrt{de} - 3\sqrt[4]{a}.$

3. $\sqrt{\dfrac{1}{ab^2c^2}}.$

4. $(a + b) - \sqrt[5]{2a} + \sqrt{\dfrac{9c^2d^2}{2\sqrt[3]{b}}}.$

5. $5\sqrt[5]{2ad} + \sqrt[4]{\dfrac{a}{2b}} - de^2.$

If $a = \frac{1}{2}$, $b = \frac{1}{3}$, $c = \frac{1}{4}$, $d = 1$, find the value of:

6. $3a - 2b + c^2 - d^2.$

7. $abc + 4\sqrt{\dfrac{1}{c^4}}.$

8. $(a + b)(c + d).$

9. $3(a - b) + \sqrt{c} - ab.$

10. $2a^2 + 3(b - c) + 2cd - \sqrt{b^2}.$

CHAPTER 8

Fractions

Fractions are an important part of a basic course of mathematics. Much work, including decimals, is based on them. A good deal of the work formerly requiring fractions is now best handled by decimals and decimal calculations.

What do we really mean by the term 'fraction'? What is meant by $\frac{1}{2}$ of something, $\frac{1}{4}$ or $\frac{3}{4}$ of something? We all know what half a cup of tea is—whether it be the top half or the bottom—and we know how many halves of a cup of tea go to make a whole one. We also know what a third of a cake is and, of course, two thirds is twice as much. For a half a cup of tea we divide the cup into two parts and drink one of them; for a third of a cake, we cut the cake into three equal pieces and eat one of them, and for two-thirds we eat two of them. The same is true of all fractions of something. A fraction consists of two parts, a top number and a bottom number (called the *numerator* and *denominator* respectively) separated by a horizontal line. To obtain a given fraction of a thing divide it into as many parts as the denominator and then take as many of them as the number that is the numerator. A fraction, then, is one or more equal parts of a thing. And this applies to metres and kilogrammes as much as to cups of tea and pieces of cake.

Improper and proper fractions

What is the meaning of such top-heavy-looking ex-
pressions as $\frac{9}{7}$, $\frac{16}{5}$, etc.? If a thing is divided into *seven*
equal parts, it is impossible to take *nine* of them. Such
forms can be called 'fractions' only for convenience—
they are **improper fractions** as opposed to **proper fractions**,
in which the numerator is smaller than the denominator.
Thus, $\frac{19}{7}$, $\frac{13}{9}$, $\frac{9}{4}$ are *improper* fractions and $\frac{1}{15}$, $\frac{1}{14}$, $\frac{3}{16}$ are
proper fractions. $\frac{9}{7}$ of £1 must mean $\frac{7}{7}$ of £1, that is the
whole £1, and $\frac{2}{7}$ of another £1. And while sometimes it
is convenient to work with such fractions as $\frac{9}{7}$, $\frac{16}{5}$, yet in
practical work you may meet these fractions in the forms
$1\frac{2}{7}$ and $3\frac{1}{5}$.

OPERATIONS WITH VULGAR FRACTIONS

Addition and subtraction of vulgar fractions

1. *When the fractions have the same denominators.*

   Example 1. Add $\frac{1}{5}$, $\frac{2}{5}$, $\frac{3}{5}$.

   Here, as the unit (it may be £1 or 1 kg) is divided in
each case into 5 equal parts, the sum of the fractions
is found by simply adding the numerators, which gives
us $\frac{6}{5}$ or $1\frac{1}{5}$, i.e. one unit and one-fifth.

   Example 2. From £$\frac{5}{8}$ take £$\frac{3}{8}$.

   Here, as the unit £1 is divided in each case into 8 equal
parts, the difference of the fractions is found by simply
finding the difference of the numerators, which gives us
$\frac{2}{8}$ of £1, or £$\frac{1}{4}$.

2. *When the fractions have different denominators.*

   Example 3. Add $\frac{1}{3}$ km, $\frac{1}{15}$ km, $\frac{2}{5}$ km, $\frac{1}{4}$ km.

   Can we, without altering the values of these fractions,

convert them into other fractions having the same denominators? The following shows that we can!

Here are three equal straight lines, the first divided into 4 equal parts, the second into 8 equal parts and the third into 12 equal parts. (See Fig. 6.)

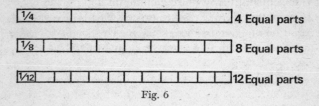

Fig. 6

It is evident that $\frac{1}{4}$ of the first line is the same length as $\frac{2}{8}$ of the second line and $\frac{3}{12}$ of the third line. In other words, when the denominator is doubled, trebled, etc., the numerator requires to be doubled, trebled, etc., in order to show the same length as before. The doubling has made the parts only *half as large* as they were originally; and to get a fraction equal to the original fraction we must *double* the *number of parts* taken. Note this fact, then, that *a fraction is not altered in value if both numerator and denominator are multiplied or divided by the same number.* Hence:

$$\left.\begin{array}{l} \frac{1}{3} \text{ km} = \frac{5}{15} \text{ km} \\ \frac{1}{15} \text{ ,, } = \frac{1}{15} \text{ ,, } \\ \frac{2}{5} \text{ ,, } = \frac{6}{15} \text{ ,, } \end{array}\right\} = \frac{12}{15}.$$

We have now to add $\frac{12}{15}$ and $\frac{1}{4}$.

Here it is not quite so evident how to proceed. But the new common denominator must be a multiple of each of the denominators 15 and 4, and, being the *lowest* common denominator (we always want the *lowest* for convenience), must therefore be the lowest common multiple of the given denominators. Find, then, the L.C.M. of 15 and 4. It is 60. $\frac{12}{15}$, then, is to be converted into a fraction whose denominator is 60; that is, a fraction whose denominator is 4 times the original denominator. Thus, on multiplying the denominator and numerator by 4, we obtain $\frac{48}{60}$. The same process with $\frac{1}{4}$ gives us $\frac{15}{60}$. Addition of $\frac{48}{60}$ and $\frac{15}{60}$ gives us $\frac{63}{60}$. This, on dividing the numerator and denominator by 3, gives us $\frac{21}{20}$ or $1\frac{1}{20}$.

Example 4.

$$\tfrac{1}{6} + \tfrac{1}{9} + \tfrac{1}{18} + \tfrac{1}{4} + \tfrac{2}{5}.$$

L.C.M. of denominators = 180.

Hence the whole expression

$$= \tfrac{30}{180} + \tfrac{20}{180} + \tfrac{10}{180} + \tfrac{45}{180} + \tfrac{72}{180},$$

or, more shortly,

$$\tfrac{30 + 20 + 10 + 45 + 72}{180} = \tfrac{177}{180}.$$

Example 5.

$$2\tfrac{1}{2} + \tfrac{3}{4} + \tfrac{7}{8} + \tfrac{5}{11}.$$

Leave the 2 out of account for the present and deal with the fractions.

L.C.M. of 2, 4, 8, 11 = 88.

$$\therefore 2\tfrac{1}{2} + \tfrac{3}{4} + \tfrac{7}{8} + \tfrac{5}{11}$$
$$= 2\tfrac{44 + 66 + 77 + 40}{88}$$
$$= 2\tfrac{227}{88}$$
$$= 2 + 2\tfrac{51}{88}$$
$$= 4\tfrac{51}{88}.$$

It has been shown that a fraction is not altered in value if both its numerator and its denominator are multiplied or divided by the same number.

The process of altering the form of the fraction by *dividing* both numerator and denominator by the same number is called *cancelling*. Its great utility in shortening calculations will appear all through the worked examples of the book. Meanwhile, the following examples will show its utility in the addition and subtraction of fractions:

Example 6. Add $\frac{36}{72}$, $\frac{15}{180}$, $\frac{98}{144}$, $\frac{17}{51}$.

Here $\frac{36}{72} = \frac{1}{2}$, $\frac{15}{180} = \frac{1}{12}$, $\frac{98}{144} = \frac{49}{72}$, $\frac{17}{51} = \frac{1}{3}$; and it is certainly easier to add $\frac{1}{2}$, $\frac{1}{12}$, $\frac{49}{72}$ and $\frac{1}{3}$ than to add the fractions in their original form. The L.C.M. of 2, 12, 72 and 3 = 72.

Thus, $\frac{1}{2} + \frac{1}{12} + \frac{49}{72} + \frac{1}{3}$
$$= \frac{36 + 6 + 49 + 24}{72}$$
$$= \frac{115}{72}.$$
$$= 1\frac{43}{72}.$$

Example 7. From the sum of $\frac{19}{38}$ and $\frac{18}{20}$ take $\frac{16}{120}$.

Here $\frac{19}{38} = \frac{1}{2}$, $\frac{18}{20} = \frac{9}{10}$, and $\frac{16}{120} = \frac{2}{15}$ and, the expression $\frac{1}{2} + \frac{9}{10} - \frac{2}{15}$ is more easily simplified than the expression $\frac{19}{38} + \frac{18}{20} - \frac{16}{120}$. The reader should complete this problem to obtain the answer $1\frac{4}{15}$.

EXERCISE 12

1. Reduce the following fractions to their simplest forms: $\frac{18}{20}$, $\frac{14}{28}$, $\frac{39}{117}$, $\frac{26}{38}$.

2. What is the difference between the following pairs of fractions: $\frac{3}{8}$ and $\frac{6}{16}$; $\frac{3}{4}$ and $\frac{4}{3}$; $\frac{8}{9}$ and $\frac{7}{8}$?

3. Add £$\frac{2}{5}$, £$\frac{5}{8}$, £$\frac{7}{25}$, £$\frac{3}{4}$.

4. Add $2\frac{3}{4}$ t, $\frac{5}{6}$ t, $\frac{7}{16}$ t, $\frac{4}{5}$ t. (t = tonne = 1000 kg.)

5. Two men own $\frac{1}{5}$ and $\frac{1}{7}$ of a business respectively. How much of the whole business do they own between them?

6. Which is the larger of the following pairs of fractions: $\frac{3}{7}$ or $\frac{4}{9}$; $\frac{12}{13}$ or $\frac{11}{14}$? (If the fractions are changed into others

having the same denominators, then the fraction with the larger numerator must be the larger.)

7. From the sum of $\frac{1}{3}$ and $\frac{1}{9}$ take $\frac{1}{15}$.

8. A sum of money is divided among three persons, A, B, C. A received $\frac{3}{16}$ of it; B receives $\frac{1}{3}$ of it. What fraction does C receive? (Evidently I *less* the sum of $\frac{3}{16}$ and $\frac{1}{3}$. Notice that I can be represented by $\frac{2}{2}$, $\frac{3}{3}$, $\frac{10}{10}$, etc.)

9. Arrange in order of magnitude the fractions $\frac{4}{7}$, $\frac{5}{9}$, $\frac{2}{3}$, $\frac{7}{8}$, $\frac{8}{9}$ and $\frac{6}{10}$.

10. A cistern can be filled by one pipe in 15 minutes, and by another in 20 minutes; in what time would both together fill it? (The pipe that fills the cistern in 15 minutes puts in $\frac{1}{15}$ in I minute.)

11. Two pipes empty a cistern in 8 and 10 hours respectively, and a third pipe fills it in 6 hours; in what time will the cistern be emptied if all three pipes are opened at the same time?

12. I have read 50 pages of a book containing 205 pages. What fraction of the book have I read, and what fraction have I still to read? (The whole unit—the book—is divided into 205 equal parts or pages, and 50 of them have been read.)

Multiplication of vulgar fractions

1. *To multiply a fraction by a whole number.*

Example 8. $\frac{3}{8} \times 2$.

Here $\frac{3}{8}$ means that the unit is divided into 8 equal parts and that 3 of these parts are taken. Therefore, 3 of these equal parts taken 2 times will = 6 eighth parts; or

$$\frac{3}{8} \times 2 = \frac{6}{8}, \text{ or 6 eighths.}$$

Hence the rule: Multiply *numerator* by the whole number.

2. *To multiply a fraction by a fraction.*

Example 9. $\frac{5}{8} \times \frac{2}{3}$, or, what is the same thing, $\frac{2}{3}$ of $\frac{5}{8}$.

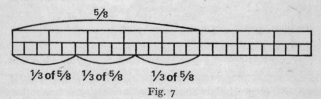

Fig. 7

Take a line divided (1) into 8 equal parts, (2) into 24 equal parts. Then from the diagram it will be seen that $\frac{1}{3}$ of $\frac{5}{8}$ is the same as $\frac{5}{24}$.

Similarly, $\frac{1}{3}$ of $\frac{2}{8} = \frac{2}{24}$, $\frac{1}{3}$ of $\frac{5}{6} = \frac{5}{18}$, etc. That is, $\frac{1}{3}$ of the fraction is got by *increasing* the denominator 3 times. Thus:

$$\frac{1}{3} \text{ of } \frac{5}{8} = \frac{5}{24};$$
$$\text{therefore } 2 \text{ times } \frac{1}{3} \text{ of } \frac{5}{8} = 2 \text{ times } \frac{5}{24}$$
$$= \frac{10}{24} \text{ (by first case).}$$

The diagram shows that this is the case.

Hence the rule: Multiply numerators for the new numerator and denominators for the new denominator.

EXERCISE 13

Find the values of:

1. 5 halves.
2. 3 sevenths.
3. 5 times $\frac{2}{3}$.
4. $8 \times \frac{3}{12}$.
5. $9 \times \frac{1}{4}$.
6. $\frac{1}{7}$ of 4.
7. $\frac{3}{5}$ of 15.
8. $\frac{3}{4}$ of 5.
9. $\frac{2}{15}$ of £75.
10. $\frac{5}{8}$ of 1 km.
11. 7 half m.
12. 9 two-fifths of 1 t.
13. $\frac{1}{2}$ of $\frac{1}{2}$.
14. $\frac{1}{5}$ of $\frac{1}{5}$.
15. $\frac{2}{3}$ of $\frac{1}{4}$.
16. $\frac{3}{4}$ of $\frac{2}{5}$.
17. $\frac{1}{2}$ of $\frac{3}{4}$ of 1 m.
18. $\frac{2}{3}$ of $\frac{6}{16}$ of 1 km.
19. $\frac{3}{4}$ of $2\frac{1}{2}$.
20. $\frac{5}{8}$ of $7\frac{1}{2}$ t.
21. $\frac{3}{5}$ of $40\frac{1}{2}$ square metres.
22. $\frac{7}{8}$ of £35·50.
23. $\frac{9}{10}$ of $35\frac{1}{4}$ litres.
24. $\frac{4}{7}$ of $3\frac{1}{2}$p.

Division of vulgar fractions

1. *To divide a fraction by a whole number.*

Example 10. $\frac{5}{8}$ divided by 4, or expressed thus: $\frac{5}{8} \div 4$.

We have already seen that in *multiplying* $\frac{5}{8}$ by 4 we simply multiply the numerator and leave the denominator unchanged. Hence in dividing $\frac{5}{8}$ by 4 the direct way would be to *divide* the numerator by 4 and leave the denominator unchanged. Now, were the fraction $\frac{12}{8}$ this would easily be done, and we should have $\frac{12}{8} \div 4 = \frac{3}{8}$. But in the case of $\frac{5}{8}$ and other fractions whose numerators are not exactly divisible by the divisor, this method is not so convenient. In the case of $\frac{5}{8}$ we should have as a result $\frac{\frac{5}{4}}{8}$, or $1\frac{1}{4}$ eighths. But to divide the numerator of a fraction has the same effect on the fraction as to multiply the denominator; that is, doubling or halving the *number* of parts taken is the same thing as halving or doubling the *size* of the parts. And so to divide $\frac{5}{8}$ by 4 it is more convenient to multiply the denominator by 4; that is, we multiply the fraction by the *divisor inverted*, or turned upside down.

Illustrations: $\frac{3}{4} \div 7 = \frac{3}{28}$; $\frac{5}{6} \div 3 = \frac{5}{18}$; $\frac{2}{5} \div 6 = \frac{2}{30} = \frac{1}{15}$.

2. *To divide a fraction by a fraction*.

Example 11. $\frac{3}{8} \div \frac{2}{5}$
$$\frac{3}{8} \div 2 = \frac{3}{16} \text{ (first case).}$$

But the real divisor is not 2 but $\frac{2}{5}$, that is, only $\frac{1}{5}$ of 2; hence the result $\frac{3}{16}$ will be 5 times too small. Therefore, we must increase it 5 times, that is, we must take $\frac{3}{16}$ 5 times, that is $\frac{15}{16}$.

Hence the rule: To divide a fraction by a fraction, *invert the divisor, and multiply* (as in multiplication of fractions).

Example 12. (1) $\frac{3}{4} \div \frac{2}{3} = \frac{3}{4} \times \frac{3}{2} = \frac{9}{8}$.
(2) $\frac{5}{6} \div \frac{7}{8} = \frac{5}{6} \times \frac{8}{7} = \frac{40}{42} = \frac{20}{21}$.

The same rule will, of course, apply in dividing a whole number by a fraction.

Example 13. (1) $10 \div \frac{1}{2} = 10 \times 2 = 20$.
(2) $5 \div \frac{3}{4} = 5 \times \frac{4}{3} = \frac{20}{3} = 6\frac{2}{3}$.

EXERCISE 14

Find the values of:

1. $\frac{5}{8}$ divided by 3.
2. $\frac{5}{6} \div 7$.
3. $\frac{4}{15} \div 5$.
4. $\frac{8}{12} \div 6$.
5. $\frac{13}{14} \div 5$.
6. $10 \div \frac{1}{3}$.
7. $16 \div \frac{3}{4}$.
8. $\frac{5}{7} \div \frac{6}{8}$.
9. $\frac{3}{8} \div \frac{7}{5}$.

10. If $\frac{5}{8}$ of a piece of property is divided equally between three people, what fraction of the property does each get?

11. How many three-quarters of a metre are there in 60 m?

12. Along a road 1260 m long posts are to be placed $3\frac{1}{2}$ m apart; how many posts will be required?

13. A piece of wire is $51\frac{1}{2}$ cm long; how many lengths of $\frac{3}{4}$ cm can be cut off it?

14. How often will a coil of rope 205 m long go round a cylinder $1\frac{1}{2}$ m in circumference?

CHAPTER 9

Simple Algebraic Fractions

A very little knowledge of algebraic fractions goes a long way in ordinary practical requirements, and what knowledge is needed is so very like that in Arithmetic that the student has really very little new to learn. We shall treat the processes in as short a way as possible.

Reduction

This is performed as in Arithmetic by *cancelling*, thus:

(1) $\dfrac{3a}{9ab} = \dfrac{1}{3b}$ cancelling $3a$, the common factor of numerator and denominator.

(2)
$$\frac{\overset{4}{\cancel{16x^2y^2z^3}}}{\underset{y}{\cancel{4y^3}}} = \frac{4x^2z^3}{y}.$$

Addition and subtraction

Example 1. $\qquad \dfrac{a}{b} + \dfrac{2a}{3b}.$

As in Arithmetic, first express all the fractions as fractions with the *same denominator*, then add the numerators, thus:

$$\frac{3a}{3b} + \frac{2a}{3b} = \frac{5a}{3b}, \text{ or } \frac{3a + 2a}{3b} = \frac{5a}{3b}.$$

Example 2.

$$\frac{x}{4} + \frac{x}{8} + \frac{2x}{3} = \frac{6x + 3x + 16x}{24} = \frac{25x}{24}.$$

Example 3.

$$\frac{7x}{8} \times \frac{x}{12} - \frac{x}{9} = \frac{63x + 6x - 8x}{72} = \frac{69x - 8x}{72} = \frac{61x}{72}.$$

Multiplication and division

As in Arithmetic, thus:

Example 4.

$$\frac{3xy}{2} \times \frac{7x^2y^2}{3x^2} = \frac{7xy^3}{2}.$$

Example 5.

$$\frac{b^2}{4} \times \frac{abc}{2b^3} \div \frac{3b^2x}{4} = \frac{b^2}{4} \times \frac{abc}{2b^3} \times \frac{4}{3b^2x} \text{ (divisor inverted)}.$$

$$= \frac{ac}{6b^2x}.$$

EXERCISE 15

Reduce the following to their simplest forms:

1. $\frac{5x}{20y}, \frac{14x^2}{2xy}, \frac{18x^3}{36y^3}.$

2. $\frac{abc}{b^2}, \frac{cde}{d}, \frac{p^2q^2}{q^3}.$

3. $\frac{6pqr}{2q^2r^2}, \frac{18lmn}{l^2}, \frac{16s^2v}{4v^3}.$

4. $\frac{x}{2} + \frac{x}{3}.$

5. $\frac{14x}{3} + \frac{x}{8}.$

6. $\frac{m}{8} - \frac{n}{12}.$

7. $\frac{pq}{r} + \frac{2pq}{r^2}.$

8. $\frac{x}{3} + \frac{x}{6} - \frac{x}{8}.$

9. $\frac{2x}{3} + \frac{3x}{4} - \frac{4x}{5}.$

10. $\frac{a^2b^2}{3} + \frac{2a^2b^2}{9} - a^2b^2.$

11. $\dfrac{3xy}{2} \times 7y^2 \times \dfrac{8}{5x}$.

12. $\dfrac{12pq}{p^2} \times \dfrac{3p^3}{2} \div \dfrac{4p^4}{3}$.

13. $\dfrac{abc}{m} \times \dfrac{b^2}{n} \div pq$.

14. $\dfrac{a^3}{b^3} \times \dfrac{b^3}{a^3} \div (-ab)$.

15. $\dfrac{15b^2}{40} \times \dfrac{2px}{p^2} \times 3bx$.

16. $\dfrac{ab}{c^2} \times (-30a^2b^2) \times \dfrac{7c^3}{b} \div b^3$.

CHAPTER 10

Decimals

We can be saved the trouble of dealing with fractions having different denominators by the use of fractions having *always* as their denominators 10, 100, 1000, etc. Let us explain a little further.

In our arithmetical notation, or method of numbering, 1111 means 1000 and 100 and 10 and 1; or arranged thus:

$$
\begin{array}{r}
1000 \\
100 \\
10 \\
1 \\
\hline
1111
\end{array}
$$

In the above number we consider each figure as being *ten* times as valuable as the neighbouring right-hand figure. Similarly, $5643 = 5000 + 600 + 40 + 3$, that is, $3 + 10$ times $4 + 100$ times $6 + 1000$ times 5.

Now, supposing we reckon from the unit's place *towards the right*, the first place to the right of the unit would be *one-tenth* of the value of the unit's place, the second place would be one-tenth of the value of the first place, and so on. Then, if we insert some mark (a dot) to distinguish between the unit and the tenth of the unit, the expression 111·111 will mean $100 + 10 + 1 + \frac{1}{10} + \frac{1}{100} + \frac{1}{1000}$.

Such a system is most useful, especially when the various measures are based on this system: and this is true of both the metric system and the decimal currency system. But it is also useful in ordinary calculations. Its full usefulness will rapidly become apparent.

OPERATIONS WITH DECIMALS

Addition and subtraction of decimal fractions

A decimal fraction is one in which the denominator is 10, 100, 1000, etc.; that is, 10 or some power of 10. These fractions are simply extensions of the ordinary whole numbers; and their addition, subtraction, multiplication and division are performed in the same way as the addition, etc., of whole numbers.

The following will help you to understand the method of addition and subtraction: First, 3564·893 means three thousands, five hundreds, six tens, four units, eight tenths, nine hundredths, three thousands; or expressed thus:

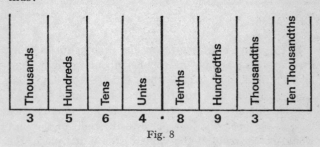

Fig. 8

Consequently, if we wish to add to this any similar number or numbers, all we have to do is to see, as in ordinary addition, that units are placed beneath units, tens beneath tens, tenths beneath tenths and so on. This will easily be done if we take care to *place the decimal points under each other*. The same will hold good with regard to subtraction.

Example 1. Add 5·75, 845·6, 9·3051, 815·5, 7192·83, 0·000 05.

$$
\begin{array}{r}
5·75 \\
845·6 \\
9·3051 \\
815·5 \\
7192·83 \\
0·000\ 05 \\
\hline
8868·985\ 15
\end{array}
$$

Example 2. From 815·62 take 75·814.

$$
\begin{array}{r}
815·62 \\
75·814 \\
\hline
739·806
\end{array}
$$

Example 3. From 0·001 take 0·000 09

$$
\begin{array}{r}
0·001 \\
0·000\ 09 \\
\hline
0·000\ 91
\end{array}
$$

EXERCISE 16

Add together:

1. 0·056, 9·934, 19·84, 17·65.
2. 0·005, 15·6, 81·3, 0·0009.
3. 14·375, 19·005, 81·652, 17·01.
4. 642·0005, 9023·6, 84·000 95, 72·34, 0·000 05.
5. 180·9102, 1875·03, 123·123, 0·000 919, 0·01, 0·023, 0·345.

Subtract:

6. 8 from 8·75.
7. 19 from 26·837 05.
8. 113·1 from 115·75.
9. 27·01 from 38·001.
10. 0·0005 from 0·005.

Multiplication of decimals

In multiplication you proceed as in the case of whole numbers. The only new thing to notice is the *placing of the decimal point*.

The following will explain:

$$0\cdot5 \times 0\cdot3 = 5 \text{ tenths} \times 3 \text{ tenths}$$
$$= 15 \text{ hundredths}$$
$$= 0\cdot15.$$
$$0\cdot25 \times 0\cdot3 = 25 \text{ hundredths} \times 3 \text{ tenths}$$
$$= 75 \text{ thousandths}$$
$$= 0\cdot075.$$

In this way you will see *that the number of decimal places in the product is always equal to the number in the multiplicand + the number in the multiplier.*

Example 4. $784\cdot623 \times 0\cdot34$.

$$
\begin{array}{r}
784\,623 \\
34 \\
\hline
3\,138\,492 \\
23\,538\,69 \\
\hline
26\,677\,182 \\
\end{array}
$$

Here 3 in the multiplicand is in the third decimal place, and 4 in the multiplier is in the second decimal place; hence the product of 3 by 4 will be in the fifth decimal place; that is, 2 in the product must be five places to the right of the decimal point. Hence the point must be between 6 and 7, and the answer is $266\cdot771\,82$.

Example 5. $0\cdot0005 \times 0\cdot003$.

$$
\begin{array}{r}
5 \\
3 \\
\hline
15 \\
\end{array}
$$

Here 5 must be in the seventh decimal place, and so 5 'noughts' must be placed between 1 and the point, thus, 0·000 001 5.

Absurd answers often arise from a misplacing of the point. A good way to avoid these is to test your answer if possible by a mental calculation with vulgar fractions. Thus, supposing we have to multiply 0·56 by 12, 0·56 × 12 = 6·72.

Now, 0·56 is almost = $\frac{1}{2}$, and $\frac{1}{2}$ of 12 = 6, which proves that the result 6·72 is correct as far as the whole number is concerned.

Division of decimals

In dividing one quantity by another when decimals are concerned in one or both, you proceed as in ordinary division. The small difficulty again, as in multiplication, is where to place the point.

First we multiply or divide the divisor by the power of 10 (10, 100, 1000, etc.) needed to bring the decimal point after the last figure and, of course, multiply the dividend also by the same power of 10. As already explained, this can be done by shifting the decimal point in each case the same number of places to right or left.

Thus, in finding 845·75 ÷ 25·3 we actually work out 8457·5 ÷ 253, or in dividing 63 by 0·0036 we work out 630 000 ÷ 36.

The division then proceeds as usual, and the decimal point can be placed in the quotient by inspection (or common sense). Thus if 7·81, 7810, 0·007 81 are divided by 4, the decimal places in the quotients clearly have exactly the same positions as they have in the dividends. The quotients are, in fact, 1·9525, 1952·5, 0·001 952 5. If, on the other hand, we had been dividing 2·81, 2810,

0·002 81 by 4, the decimal points would all have been one place further to the left: 0·7025, 702·5, 0·000 702 5. (The difference between the two cases is that 7 is greater than 4, while 2 is less.) In these cases with a simple divisor there is no difficulty. The principle is, however, exactly the same when the divisor, instead of being 4, is, for example, 4·736. Thus 7·81 ÷ 4·736 is 1·..., and 0·002 81 ÷ 4·736 is 0·0005 . . .

Example 6. 845·75 ÷ 25·3.

$$
\begin{array}{r}
33\cdot42 \\
253\overline{)8475\cdot5} \\
759 \\
\hline
867 \\
759 \\
\hline
1085 \\
1012 \\
\hline
730 \\
506 \\
\hline
\end{array}
$$

Example 7. 0·356 ÷ 116·4.

$$
\begin{array}{r}
0\cdot003\ 05 \\
1164\overline{)3\cdot560\ 00} \\
3\ 492 \\
\hline
6\ 800 \\
5\ 820 \\
\hline
\end{array}
$$

As a rule, there is no point in carrying decimals to more than three or four places. When it comes to measuring tenths, etc., of centimetres, you can readily see how errors will creep in from the use of defective instruments, from errors of observation and from inaccurate measurements; so that if an error is made in the *first* decimal place you are only increasing it by carrying your calculations beyond this place. The reader should note that in Examples 1 and 2 the answers obtained are correct to one decimal place *less* than the number shown in the answer. This will be explained in more detail later.

In connection with multiplication and division of decimals keep the following well in mind:

(1) In multiplying a decimal by 10, 100, etc., it is evident that all we have to do is to move the decimal point *to the right*, one place if multiplying by 10, two places if by 100 and so on. Thus:

$$54 \cdot 26 \times 10 = 542 \cdot 6,$$
$$0 \cdot 005 \times 100 = 0 \cdot 5,$$
$$8 \cdot 6 \times 1000 = 8600.$$

(2) In dividing a decimal by 10, 100, etc., we move the decimal point *to the left*. Thus:

$$84 \cdot 6 \div 10 = 8 \cdot 46,$$
$$0 \cdot 89 \div 100 = 0 \cdot 0089,$$
$$175 \cdot 32 \div 1000 = 0 \cdot 175 \ 32.$$

EXERCISE 17

1. Multiply 87·4 by 0·005.
2.   ,,   7·1 by 8·35.
3.   ,,   90·09 by 8·001.
4.   ,,   0·0009 by 0·006.
5.   ,,   1009·575 by 7·65.
6.   ,,   0·007 by 1000.
7. Divide 0·875 by 0·23.
8.   ,,   91 by 0·005.

9. ,, 17·32 by 0·004.
10. ,, 1·001 by 100.
11. ,, 875 by 0·53.
12. ,, 150 by 0·150.
13. ,, 0·008 75 by 25.
14. ,, 6·15 by 2·3.

15. How many times can 0·015 be subtracted from 853, and what is the remainder?

16. A roller 1·25 m in circumference makes 35 revolutions in passing from one end of a bowling green to the other. What is the length of the bowling green?

17. Add together 0·55 of a week, 0·36 of a day and 0·72 of an hour, and express the result in hours.

18. The length of a strip of plate is 16·25 cm long. How many pieces 0·12 cm long can be cut off from it, and what will be the length of the odd bit?

Discarding of certain decimals in practical work

In practical work it is often unnecessary to carry the decimal operations to more than one or two decimal places. The result will not be strictly correct; but since at the very best it is impossible to be perfectly exact with our *measurements*, our calculations will not be so far out. In discarding certain of the decimals, therefore, we must simply try to do so with the least possible error. For example, if a result came out as 1·5736 and we wished to retain only one decimal place, 1·6 would be a more correct result than 1·5 for 0·57 is *nearer* 0·60 than 0·50. Again, if we wished to retain two decimal places, 1·57 would be a more correct result than 1·58, for 0·57 is *nearer* 0·573 than 0·580. The rule, then, we adopt is: (1) to increase the last figure retained by 1 if the next figure is 5 or more than 5; (2) to leave the last figure unchanged if the next figure is below 5.

Example of the application of the idea:

Add 0·5723, 8·653, 5·4297, 14·0053 so as to retain two places of decimals.

Ordinary method	*Contracted method*
0·5723	0·57
8·653	8·65
5·4297	5·43
14·0053	14·01
28·6603	28·66

Here the *contracted* result differs from the *actual* result by 0·0003 (28·6603 *minus* 28·66); that is, by $\frac{3}{10000}$.

Contracted methods are also employed in multiplication and division of *long* decimals. As ordinary practical life seldom, if ever, calls for multiplication and division with lengthy decimals, the contracted methods are not included in this volume.

Application of fractions

The following examples illustrate some of the methods of dealing with concrete quantities:

Example 1. To express one quantity as a fraction of another, say £5·37½ of £50.

Just as ½ expresses the fraction which 1 is of 2, or ¾ the fraction which 3 is of 4, so $\frac{£5·37\frac{1}{2}}{£50}$ expresses the fraction which £5·37½ is of £50.

Of course, this fraction must be simplified in order to make it more definite. Thus:

$$\frac{£5·37\frac{1}{2}}{£50} = \frac{5\frac{3}{8}}{50} = \frac{\frac{43}{8}}{50} = \frac{43}{8} \times \frac{1}{50} = \frac{43}{400}.$$

£5·37½, then, is $\frac{43}{400}$ of £50.

Example 2. Reduce £3·62½ to a fraction of £1.

$$\text{The fraction} = \frac{\pounds 3 \cdot 62\frac{1}{2}}{\pounds 1}$$

$$= \frac{\pounds 3\frac{5}{8}}{\pounds 1}$$

$$= \frac{29}{8} = 3\frac{5}{8}.$$

The answer $3\frac{5}{8}$ means that $\pounds 3 \cdot 62\frac{1}{2}$ is $3\frac{5}{8}$ times $\pounds 1$.

Example 3. What fraction of 14 t is 1·24 kg?

$$\text{The fraction} = \frac{1 \cdot 24 \text{ kg}}{14 \text{ t}}$$

$$= \frac{1240 \text{ g}}{14 \text{ 000 000 g}}$$

$$= \frac{0 \cdot 001 \ 24}{14}$$

$$= \frac{0 \cdot 000 \ 62}{7}$$

$$= 0 \cdot 000 \ 096.$$

Application of decimals

Example 4. What decimal of $\pounds 5$ is $\pounds 4 \cdot 20$?

$$\text{The vulgar fraction} = \frac{\pounds 4 \cdot 20}{\pounds 5}$$

$$= \frac{4\frac{1}{5}}{\pounds 5}$$

$$= \frac{21}{5} \times \frac{1}{5}$$

$$= \frac{21}{25}.$$

Therefore the decimal fraction $=$ 0·84 $=$ 0·84

$$25\overline{)21 \cdot 00} \qquad \text{exactly.}$$

$$\underline{20 \cdot 00}$$

$$\overline{1 \cdot 00}$$

$$\underline{1 \cdot 00}$$

$$\overline{0 \cdot 00}$$

Alternatively, we have that the vulgar fraction $=$
$$\frac{£4 \cdot 20}{£5 \cdot 00}.$$

In suitable cases, where the denominator is a factor of 100, we may proceed as follows:

$$\frac{4 \cdot 20}{5 \cdot 00}$$

$$= \frac{4 \cdot 20 \times 20}{5 \cdot 00 \times 20}$$

$$= \frac{84 \cdot 0}{100}$$

$$= 0 \cdot 84 \text{ exactly, as before.}$$

Example 5. To express 5·9 days in days, hours, minutes.

$$\begin{array}{r} \mathbf{5 \cdot 9} \text{ days} \\ 24 \\ \hline \mathbf{21 \cdot 6} \text{ hours} \\ 60 \\ \hline \mathbf{36 \cdot 0} \text{ minutes} \end{array}$$

∴ 5·9 days $=$ 5 days 21 hours 36 minutes, exactly.

The reasoning of the above process is as follows:

(1) 0·9 of 1 day = 0·9 of 24 hours = 0·9 × 24 hours.
(2) 0·6 of 1 hour = 0·6 of 60 minutes = 0·6 × 60 minutes.

EXERCISE 18

1. What fraction is £6·37½ of £20·37½.
2. What decimal is 5p of £4?
3. What decimal of £21 is 50p?
4. Find the value of 0·03 of £2·50.
5. What is 2·5 of £0·03?

6. Add together 0·125 of £1, 0·75 of £0·30 and 0·25 of 5p, and express the result as a decimal of £1.

7. Express 6 days 12 hours as the decimal of a week.

8. What decimal of a year is 255 days when:

(1) the year is not a leap year?
(2) it is a leap year?

9. 160·25 tonnes of coal are bought at £4·80 a tonne and sold at £5·05 a tonne. How much was gained on the transaction?

10. A man and a woman work for 40 and 30 hours a week respectively. The man's wage totals £28 and the woman's £18.

(1) What decimal is the woman's weekly wage of the man's?
(2) What decimal is the woman's hourly wage of the man's?
(3) If, as a counter to male chauvinism, the woman's hourly wage is made to equal the man's, what decimal is her *new* hourly wage of her old?

11. A Swiss 20-franc note is worth £1·614; find the value of 250·15 francs.

12. If $1 is £2·60, what decimal is 1p of 1¢?

13. If a man is going to Aland, where the rate of exchange is $A4·32 to £1 and he wishes to take not more than £300 of travellers' cheques in $As, how many will he take? (Bear in mind that travellers' cheques come only in whole $As.)

14. The force in newtons acting on someone of mass m kg in a train which is accelerating at a metres per second per second is $m \times a$.

(1) What is the force on a man of mass 83·6 kg accelerating at 12·2 m per s per s?
(2) What is the force on a budgie of mass 211 g accelerating in the same train?

CHAPTER II
Powers and Roots

We have already encountered (see chapters 1 and 3), and used, the ideas of powers and roots and, in particular, squares, cubes, square and cube roots. This chapter starts with a revision of these ideas and then develops them; make sure you understand and know the early part of the chapter before you attempt to carry on.

Previously, the ideas have largely been introduced arithmetically. Here we will use only algebra, which makes progress more difficult but much more valuable.

Powers

x^a is x multiplied by itself a times; it is read as 'x to the a' or 'ath', or 'x to the power a'.

the number (a) indicating the power is called the 'index', or 'indices' in the plural.

x^2 is read 'x squared' and x^3 as 'x cubed'.

Roots

$a\sqrt{x}$ or $a\sqrt{x}$ is the number which, when multiplied by itself a times, gives x; it is read as 'the ath root of x'.

$\sqrt[2]{x}$, or, more usually, $\sqrt{x}$, is the square root of x, and $\sqrt[3]{x}$ is the cube root of x.

The power notation is also used with units; e.g. m^3 for cubic metre.

Operations with indices

$$x^a \times x^b = x^{a+b} \qquad (1)$$
$$x^a \div x^b = x^{a-b} \qquad (2)$$

These results can be demonstrated by writing out simple examples in full. The law (1) can be generalised to give

$$(x^a)^b = x^{a \cdot b} \qquad (3)$$

Notice that $(x^a)^b \neq x^{(a^b)}$.

Extension of the index notation

It may seem fruitless to ask what the result is when we divide a number by itself: we all know the answer is 1, so why bother? We bother, of course, because it is not fruitless. Let us ask, for example, what we get when we divide x^a by x^a.

Using (2) above,

$$x^a \div x^a = x^{a-a} = x^0.$$

This result is clearly true whatever the value of a. And we know that, whatever the value of x, $x^a \div x^a = 1$, so we have:

$$\textit{whatever the value of } x, \; x^0 = 1 \qquad (4)$$

In other words, any number raised to the power zero is 1.

Negative indices

So far we have implicitly restricted the values of indices to positive whole numbers, although we have now extended this to include a zero index. We are now in a position to consider what meaning, if any, negative indices have.

If c is a positive whole number, what can x^{-c} mean? We can rewrite $-c$ as $0 - c$ and x^{-c} as x^{0-c}. Using (2), we can rewrite this as $x^0 \div x^c$; now we use (4) to rewrite the expression as $1 \div x^c$, which is $\dfrac{1}{x^c}$. Alternatively, we can consider the value of $x^c \times x^{-c}$ and use (1) to arrive at the same result, namely:

$$x^{-c} = \frac{1}{x^c} \qquad (5)$$

This explains the notation used with some units to represent division, as in ms^{-2} for $\mathrm{m/s}^2$.

Fractional indices

Finally, for this section, we can extend the idea of a power to cover the meaning of fractional indices.

Consider $x^{\frac{1}{2}} \times x^{\frac{1}{2}}$: by (1), this is x. But when a number multiplied by itself gives x, that number is, by definition, the square root of x.

More generally, by considering the value of $(x^{\frac{1}{n}})^n$ and using (1), we can show that

$$x^{1/n} = \sqrt[n]{x} \qquad (6)$$

EXERCISE 19

Find the values:

1. 4^3; 12^2; 5^4; 2^{10}.
2. $\sqrt{4}$; $\sqrt[3]{125}$; $\sqrt[4]{16}$; $\sqrt[5]{2^{10}}$.
3. 4^{-3}; 12^{-2}; 5^{-4}; 2^{-8}.
4. 2^0; 6^0; 37^0; 19^0.
5. $4^{\frac{1}{2}}$; $125^{\frac{1}{3}}$; $64^{\frac{1}{2}}$; $(2^{10})^{\frac{1}{5}}$.
6. $(4^3)^{\frac{1}{2}}$; $(4^{\frac{1}{2}})^3$; $4^{\frac{3}{2}}$; $4^{-\frac{3}{2}}$.
7. $(x^a)^{\frac{1}{b}}$; $(x^a)^b$; $(x^a)^{-\frac{1}{b}}$; $x^{\frac{a}{b}}$.
8. $27^{\frac{2}{3}}$; $27^{-\frac{2}{3}}$; $(\frac{1}{4})^{\frac{1}{2}}$; $x^{-\frac{a}{b}}$.

9. $4^{1 \cdot 5}$; $(\frac{1}{4})^{1 \cdot 5}$; $16^{0 \cdot 25}$; $32^{0 \cdot 2}$.
10. 2 is not the only square root of 4; what is the other one? All positive numbers have two square roots. If $x = \sqrt{y}$, what is the other square root of y?

We can use addition of indices as a method of multiplication even when the two numbers multiplied are not given as powers of the same number. Consider, for example, $2^{10} \times 4^9$.

$$
\begin{aligned}
\text{We know } 4^9 &= (2^2)^9 \\
&= 2^{18} && \text{(by (3))} \\
\therefore 2^{10} \times 4^9 &= 2^{10} \times 2^{18} \\
&= 2^{28} && \text{(by (1))}.
\end{aligned}
$$

Similarly,

$$
\begin{aligned}
2^{10} \times 4^9 \times 8^4 \times 16^2 &= 2^{10} \times (2^2)^9 \times (2^3)^4 \times (2^4)^2 \\
&= 2^{10} \times 2^{18} \times 2^{12} \times {}^{28} && \text{(by (3))} \\
&= 2^{48} && \text{(by (1))}.
\end{aligned}
$$

We could have solved this as

$$
\begin{aligned}
2^{10} \times 4^9 \times 8^4 \times 16^2 &= (8^{\frac{1}{3}})^{10} \times (8^{\frac{2}{3}})^9 \times 8^4 \times (8^{\frac{4}{3}})^2 \\
&= 8^{\frac{10}{3}} \times 8^6 \times 8^4 \times 8^{\frac{8}{3}} && \text{(by (3))} \\
&= 8^{16} && \text{(by (1))}.
\end{aligned}
$$

If we had solved the expression by the first method and then wanted to express the answer as a power of 8, we could have rewritten 2^{48} as $(2^3)^{16}$ by (3), which is, of course, 8^{16} as before.

Example 1. Express $5^{\frac{8}{3}} \times 25^{\frac{3}{2}} \times 125^{\frac{4}{7}} \times 625^4$ as a power of (1) 5, (2) 25.

(1) $5^{\frac{8}{3}} \times 25^{\frac{3}{2}} \times 125^{\frac{4}{7}} \times 625^4$

$$
\begin{aligned}
&= 5^{\frac{8}{3}} \times (5^2)^{\frac{3}{2}} \times (5^3)^{\frac{4}{7}} \times (5^4)^4 \\
&= 5^{\frac{8}{3}} \times 5^3 \times 5^{\frac{12}{7}} \times 5^{16} && \text{(by (3))} \\
&= 5^{\frac{407}{21}} && \text{(by (1))}.
\end{aligned}
$$

(2)
$$
\begin{aligned}
25 &= 5^2 \\
\therefore 5^{\frac{407}{21}} &= (5^2)^{\frac{407}{42}} && \text{(by (3))}.
\end{aligned}
$$

Example 2. If $3 = 2^a$ and $5 = 2^b$, express the following as powers of 2: (1) 10, (2) 6, (3) 60, (4) 3·6.

(1) $10 = 2 \times 5$ (factorising)
$$= 2^1 \times 2^b$$
$$= 2^{1+b} \qquad \text{(by (1))}.$$

(2) $6 = 2 \times 3$ (factorising)
$$= 2^1 \times 2^a$$
$$= 2^{1+a} \qquad \text{(by (1))}.$$

(3)   *First method:*
$$60 = 2^2 \times 3 \times 5 \qquad \text{(factorising)}$$
$$= 2^2 \times 2^a \times 2^b$$
$$= 2^{2+a+b} \qquad \text{(by (1))}.$$

    Second method:
$$60 = 6 \times 10 \qquad \text{(factorising)}$$
$$= 2^{1+a} \times 2^{1+b} \qquad \text{(by the results above)}$$
$$= 2^{2+a+b} \qquad \text{(by (1))}.$$

(4) $3 \cdot 6 = 2^2 \times 3^2 \div 10 \qquad \text{(factorising)}$
$$= 2^2 \times (2^a)^2 \div 2^{1+b}$$
$$= 2^{2+2a-(1+b)}$$
$$= 2^{1+2a-b}.$$

Example 3. If $2 = 10^m$, $3 = 10^n$, what power of 10 are the following: (1) 5, (2) 50, (3) 1·5, (4) 0·15, (5) 4·8?

(1) $5 = 10 \div 2$
$$= 10^1 \div 10^m$$
$$= 10^{1-m} \qquad \text{(by (2))}$$
$\therefore$ 5 is 10 to the power $(1 - m)$.

(2) $50 = 5 \times 10$
$$= 10^{1-m} \times 10^1$$
$$= 10^{2-m}$$
$\therefore$ 50 is 10 to the power $(2 - m)$.

(3) $1 \cdot 5 = 5 \times 3 \div 10$ *or* $1 \cdot 5 = 3 \div 2$
        $= 10^{1-m} \times 10^n \div 10^1$ $= 10^n \div 10^m$
        $= 10^{n-m}$ $= 10^{n-m}$

$\therefore$ $1 \cdot 5$ is 10 to the power $(n - m)$.

(4) $0 \cdot 15 = 1 \cdot 5 \div 10$
         $= 10^{n-m} \div 10^1$
         $= 10^{n-m-1}$

$\therefore$ $0 \cdot 15$ is 10 to the power $(n - m - 1)$; notice that there are many different ways of arriving at this result.

(5) $4 \cdot 8 = 2^4 \times 3 \div 10$
        $= (10^m)^4 \times 10^n \div 10^1$
        $= 10^{4m+n-1}$

$\therefore$ $4 \cdot 8$ is 10 to the power $(4m + n - 1)$.

EXERCISE 20

Express as powers of 3:

   1. $3^{\frac{3}{4}} \times 9^6 \times 27^{\frac{3}{2}} \div 243^{\frac{5}{6}}$.
   2. $(\frac{1}{9})^2 \times 3^5 \times 81^8$.
   3. Express the solutions of questions 1 and 2 as powers of 9.

If $3 = 12^a$, $5 = 12^b$, express as powers of 12:

   4. 108.
   5. 4.
   6. 2.
   7. 10.
   8. $\frac{2}{3}$.

If $3 = 10^{0 \cdot 48}$, $5 = 10^{0 \cdot 70}$, express as powers of 10:

   9. 2.
  10. 18.
  11. $1 \cdot 8$.
  12. 180.
  13. $0 \cdot 18$.
  14. $0 \cdot 018$.

Indices can usefully be used to express numbers as what are called *standard forms*. The standard form will be particularly useful in the next chapter.

When a number is written in standard form, it is written as the product of two numbers, one of which has only one digit in the whole number part and the other of which is a whole-number power of 10. For example:

Number	Standard form
276	$2 \cdot 76 \times 10^2$
27·6	$2 \cdot 76 \times 10^1$
2·76	$2 \cdot 76 \times 10^0$
2 760	$2 \cdot 76 \times 10^3$
27 600	$2 \cdot 76 \times 10^4$
0·276	$2 \cdot 76 \times 10^{-1}$
452	$4 \cdot 52 \times 10^2$
7 468·32	$7 \cdot 468 \ 32 \times 10^3$

When two numbers in standard form are multiplied, divided, etc., you must remember the rules of indices.

Example 4.
$$(1 \cdot 2 \times 10^4) \times (2 \cdot 3 \times 10^3) = (10^4 \times 10^3) \times (1 \cdot 2 \times 2 \cdot 3)$$
$$= 10^7 \times 2 \cdot 76.$$

Example 5.
$$(4 \cdot 8 \times 10^8) \div (1 \cdot 6 \times 10^{-3}) = (4 \cdot 8 \div 1 \cdot 6) \times (10^8 \div 10^{-3})$$
$$= 3 \times 10^{11}.$$

CHAPTER 12

Logs

The mathematics we have developed so far, and especially in the last chapter, puts us in a very strong position to simplify some of the more tedious operations in arithmetic.

Given that $3 = 10^{0.48}$ and $5 = 10^{0.70}$, we can express many more numbers as powers of 10. You should already have done this for some numbers in Exercise 20 on page 84. The table below gives some of the two-figure numbers from 2 to 10 and their equivalent powers of 10: they can all be calculated in the familiar way.

N*	P†	N	P
1·0	0·00	4·5	0·66
1·2	0·08	4·8	0·68
1·5	0·18	5·0	0·70
1·6	0·20	6·0	0·78
1·8	0·26	6·4	0·80
2·0	0·30	7·2	0·86
2·4	0·38	7·5	0·88
2·5	0·40	8·0	0·90
2·7	0·43	8·1	0·91
3·0	0·48	9·0	0·95
3·2	0·50	9·6	0·98
3·6	0·56	10·0	1·00
4·0	0·60		

* N—number.
† P—index of the power of 10 which is N; $10^P = N$.

We can see at once that, as N increases, P increases—in other words, if $N_1 = 10^{P2}$, $N_2 = 10^{P2}$ and $N_1 > N_2$, then

$P_1 > P_2$. Now, using this fact and the table we can perform some approximate calculations.

Example 1.

$$4{\cdot}5 \times 2 = 10^{0 \cdot 66} \times 10^{0 \cdot 30}$$
$$= 10^{0 \cdot 96}.$$

Looking down the **P** column to find 0·96 we find that 0·95 is the nearest number to it, and it is opposite 9·0, which is what we would hope. But it is clear that this method is only approximate and, in this case, no simpler than doing the ordinary multiplication.

But with a more difficult multiplication the addition would remain just as simple.

We can also extend the table by this sort of multiplication. 6·4 × 3·6 is approximately 23, but from the table

$$6{\cdot}4 \times 3{\cdot}6 = 10^{0 \cdot 80} \times 10^{0 \cdot 56}$$
$$= 10^{1 \cdot 36}$$
$$= 10 \times 10^{0 \cdot 36}$$

and $(10 \times 10^{0 \cdot 36})$ is 23, approximately, so we can enter 2·3 in the **N** column and 0·36 in the **P** column. This is roughly what we would expect, since 0·36 is just less than 0·38, which is opposite 2·4.

If we wished to find 64 × 36, we could rewrite the numbers in standard form and then use the table.

$$64 \times 36 = (6{\cdot}4 \times 10) \times (3{\cdot}6 \times 10)$$
$$= (6{\cdot}4 \times 3{\cdot}6) \times 10^{2}$$
$$= 10^{0 \cdot 80} \times 10^{0 \cdot 56} \times 10^{2}$$
$$= 10^{3 \cdot 36}$$
$$= 10^{3} \times 10^{0 \cdot 36}.$$

We can now look up 0·36 in the **P** column and, of course, we find 2·3 opposite it, so 64 × 36 is about $10^{3} \times 2{\cdot}3$, or 2300.

The table that we have developed is quite simple, and we could easily extend it so that we included, in the **N** column, all the numbers from 1 to 10 with one decimal place. We could then do operations involving multiplication (including division, extracting roots, etc.) with any two-figure numbers (wherever the decimal point falls). All we need to do is to reduce the numbers to standard form and use the tables in the same way as we have done so far.

The answers we get from a table of this sort will naturally be no more than approximate: they will certainly not be accurate enough to be truly useful. For practical purposes we would need tables that gave at least four figures in the **N** and **P** columns; such tables have been compiled.

Such tables have usually been constructed with 10 as the base (i.e. they are '**N** = 10^P' tables) and the logic of this should be clear. By using 10 as the base, we can easily reduce our **N**-numbers to a form in which the tables can be very simply used: standard form. These tables, then, give the indices which indicate for all numbers— within the scope of the tables—the powers they are of 10.

If **N** = 10^P, as in the table, then **P** is the index of the power of 10 which is equal to **N**. This expression is, to say the least, rather cumbersome and so we introduce a new shortland: which is what, by now, you should expect in mathematics.

Instead of writing 'the index of the power of 10 which is equal to **N**', we write *log* **N**. 'Log' is the abbreviation of 'logarithm'—a choice of word which can only be explained historically. So, if **N** = 10^P, then **P** = log **N**.

The definition of 'logarithm' is actually more general than we have suggested. We can define 'logarithm', and the word 'base', as follows:

The logarithm of a number to base a is the index of the power to which a must be raised to give the number.

a may be any number and the base of a system of logs is indicated by a small subscript after the word 'log'.

So, if $x = a^y$, then $\log_a x = y$. As we have indicated, when the base is 10 and there is no possibility of confusion, the base is omitted.

In our table we can now replace the '**P**' by the word 'log', and what the table now tells us is that, for example, $\log_{10} 4 \cdot 0 = 0 \cdot 60$ (approximately) or, more usually, $\log 4 \cdot 0 = 0 \cdot 60$. Similarly, since $1024 = 2^{10}$, $\log_2 1024 = 10$; since $81 = 3^4$, $\log_3 81 = 4$.

The whole number part of the log is called the *characteristic*; the decimal part is called the *mantissa*.

The characteristic of the log of any number to base 10 can be simply worked out by reducing the number to standard form; we know that $\log_{10} 10^n = n$, and that any number between 1 and 10 has a log to base 10 between 0 and 1. You will soon be able to work out the characteristics with ease: notice that it is always 1 less than the number of digits in the whole number part of the number whose log you are finding.

Thus in $\log_{10} 2769 \cdot 8$ the characteristic is 3
$\qquad \log_{10} 276 \cdot 98$,,   ,,   2
$\qquad \log_{10} 2 \cdot 7698$,,   ,,   0.

Since the characteristic can be worked out so easily by 'inspection' it is not given in tables of logs to base 10.

In tables the mantissa is usually calculated to at least four places of decimals. The tables give *only the mantissa*. For example, looking up 2770 we would find the mantissa is 4425, in fact $0 \cdot 4425$. This is $\log_{10} 2 \cdot 770$. The characteristic is 3 and so $\log_{10} 2770$ is $3 \cdot 4425$.

In other words, you should be able to see (and prove) that numbers consisting of the same figures have the same mantissa in their logs to base 10.

Using these techniques to find the characteristic and mantissa of logs, you should have no difficulty in using log tables.

Below is a section of the four-figure log tables printed at the end of the book.

Proportional Parts

25	3979	3997	4014	4031	4048	4065	4082	4099	4116	4133	2	3	5	7	9 10	12 14 15
26	4150	4166	4183	4200	4216	4232	4249	4265	4281	4298	2	3	5	7	8 10	11 13 15
27	4314	4330	4346	4362	4378	4393	4409	4425	4440	4456	2	3	5	6	8 9	11 13 14
28	4472	4487	4502	4518	4533	4548	4564	4579	4594	4609	2	3	5	6	8 9	11 12 14
29	4624	4639	4654	4669	4683	4698	4713	4728	4742	4757	1	3	4	6	7 9	10 12 13

(a)   (b)

The figures in column *a* in the complete table are the numbers from 1 to 99. The corresponding number (reading along the row) in column *b* is the mantissa of the logarithm. The characteristic is not given, as you know, but is written down from inspection. Thus log 27 = 1·4314, log 270 = 2·4314, etc.

If the number has a *third* significant figure, the mantissa is found in the appropriate column of the next nine columns. Thus log 27·6 = 1·4409, log 276 = 2·4409, etc.

If the number has a *fourth* significant figure, we must go to the columns headed 'Proportional Parts'. The number found in the appropriate column must be *added to* the mantissa found for the first three figures. If we want log 27·69, we look up the mantissa for log 27·6: 0·4409. For the fourth figure, 9, we find 14 in the appropriate column of the Proportional Parts. Adding this to 0·4409 we obtain 0·4423 as the mantissa. And so log 27·69 = 1·4423.

After we have completed any operation using logs, we will be left with a number which is the log of the answer we are seeking. We might, for example, know that the log of our answer is 1·4108. We could proceed by 'working back' through the log tables, as we did with our P–N table, and we would discover that the answer is 25·75. But the process is tedious and unreliable.

Instead, we are usually provided with tables which give the numbers corresponding to given logarithms; these are called anti-logarithms. The anti-log tables are used in the same way as the log-tables, but remember:

(1) that only the mantissa of the log is given in the table;
(2) that when the significant figures of the anti-log have been found, you must fix the position of the decimal point by using the rules we have considered for the characteristic.

For example, suppose that we have to find anti-log 2·3714. First we find the number listed in the anti-log table under 0·3714, which is 2352. These are the first four significant figures of the number required. Since the characteristic is 2, we must multiply this number *in standard form* by 10^2, i.e. $2·352 \times 10^2$, which is 235·2.

EXERCISE 21

(*Note: All logs are to base 10 unless otherwise stated.*)

1. Write down the characteristics of the logs of: 17; 1706; 47 194; 634; 7; 700 000; 61·49; 6784·3; 4·914; 3·65.

2. From the tables (at the back of the book) what are the logs of:

    (1) 6; 60; 600; 60 000.
    (2) 4·7; 470; 47 000.
    (3) 3·65; 365; 3650.
    (4) 17·65; 176·5; 17 650.
    (5) 1·414; 1465; 6972.

3. From the tables (at the back of the book) what are the anti-logs of:

(1) 2·67; 4·67; 1·67.
(2) 1·876; 3·876; 0·876.
(3) 0·2222; 2·2222; 4·2222.
(4) 3·0196; 3·019; 0·3019.

In using logs for calculations we must be guided by the laws which govern operations with them. Since logarithms are indices, these laws must be the same in principle as those of indices. They follow directly from the corresponding index laws. Use the index laws to prove that for any p and q:

$$\log (p \times q) = \log p + \log q;$$
$$\log (p \div q) = \log p - \log q;$$
$$\log a^n = n \log a;$$
$$\log \frac{n}{a} = \frac{1}{n} \log a.$$

Example 2. Find the value of $57·86 \times 4·385$.

Let $x = 57·86 \times 4·385$
then $\log x = \log 57·86 + \log 4·385$
$= 1·7624 + 0·6420$
$= 2·4044$
$= \log 253·7$
$\therefore x = 253·7.$

No	Log
57·86	1·7624
4·385	0·6420
253·7	2·4044

[Remember that the logs in the tables are only correct to four significant figures, so you cannot be sure of four significant figures in the answer; it would be more correct to give the answer as 254, correct to three significant figures. The method of setting out calculations with logs, shown on the right above, is likely to make your work much simpler and systematic.]

Example 3. Find the value of $\dfrac{5\cdot672 \times 18\cdot94}{1\cdot758}$.

Let $x = \dfrac{5\cdot672 \times 18\cdot94}{1\cdot758}$

No	Log
5·672	0·7538
18·94	1·2774
	2·0312
1·758	0·2450
61·12	1·7862

then $\log x = \log 5\cdot762 + \log 18\cdot94 -$
$\qquad \log 1\cdot758$
$\qquad = 0\cdot7538 + 1\cdot2774 - 0\cdot2450$
$\qquad = 1\cdot7862$
$\qquad = \log 61\cdot12$
$\therefore x = 61\cdot12$ or $61\cdot1$ (to three
$\qquad$ significant figures).

Example 4. Find the fifth root of $721\cdot8$.

Let $x = \sqrt[5]{721\cdot8}$
$\qquad = (721\cdot8)^{\frac{1}{5}}$
then $\log x = (\tfrac{1}{5}) \log 721\cdot8$
$\qquad = (\tfrac{1}{5})(2\cdot8584)$
$\qquad = 0\cdot5717$
$\therefore x = 3\cdot730$.

EXERCISE 22

Use logs to find the values of the following:

1. $47\cdot9 \times 23\cdot78$.
2. $62\cdot5 \times 97\cdot54$.
3. $22\cdot23 \times 56\cdot56 \times 27\cdot63$.
4. $6\cdot328 \times 109\cdot8$.
5. $42\cdot82 \div 19\cdot68$.
6. $65\cdot35 \div 5\cdot342$.
7. $87\cdot69 \times 43\cdot21 \div 31\cdot76$.
8. $654\cdot3 \div 7\cdot458$.
9. $\dfrac{16\cdot27 \times 8\cdot42 \times 11\cdot38}{6\cdot437 \times 45\cdot96}$.
10. $(7\cdot638)^3$.
11. $(23\cdot47)^2$.
12. $(19\cdot57)^2 \times 6\cdot67$.
13. $\dfrac{(21\cdot4)^2 \times 543}{(61\cdot2)^3}$.

14. $\dfrac{5683}{(46\cdot29)^2 \div (3\cdot76)^3}$

15. $\sqrt[4]{16\cdot42}.$

16. $\sqrt[3]{1\cdot414 \times 1\cdot63^2}$

17. $\sqrt[4]{3\cdot76 \times 4\cdot986}.$

18. If $\pi r^2 = 81$, find r ($\pi = 3\cdot142$).

19. If $\frac{4}{3}\pi r^3 = 56\cdot4$, find r.

20. If $\frac{1}{2}mv^2 = 27\cdot89$, find v when m is $3\cdot2$.

So far we have only considered powers of 10 when the index is a positive integer. We can consider cases in which the index is negative.

Thus $\begin{aligned} &10^1 &= 10 \qquad &\text{and} \quad &\log 10 &= 1 \\ &10^0 &= 1 \qquad &\text{and} \quad &\log 1 &= 0 \\ &10^{-1} = \tfrac{1}{10} &= 0\cdot1 \qquad &\text{and} \quad &\log 0\cdot1 &= -1 \\ &10^{-2} &= 0\cdot01 \qquad &\text{and} \quad &\log 0\cdot01 &= -2, \text{ etc.} \end{aligned}$

From these results we may deduce that the logs of numbers between 0 and 1 are always *negative*.

We already know that when a number is divided by 10 we obtain the log of the result by subtracting 1 from the original log.

So, $\begin{aligned} \log 49\cdot8 &= 1\cdot6972 \\ \log 4\cdot98 &= 0\cdot6972 \\ \log 0\cdot498 &= 0\cdot6972 - 1 \\ \log 0\cdot0498 &= 0\cdot6972 - 2, \text{ etc.} \end{aligned}$

From this we have that $\log 0\cdot498 = 0\cdot6972 - 1 = -0\cdot3028$. Compare these results with the answers to questions 13 and 14 in exercise 20.

But for numbers which are greater than 1 the mantissae of the logs remain the same when the numbers are multiplied or divided by 10: with the same significant figures we have the same mantissae. It is obviously going to be to our advantage if we can make sure that the same thing happens even for numbers less than 1, so that we don't end up having to write log 0·498 as −0·3028.

We can do this by not carrying out the subtraction shown above and writing *only the characteristic as negative*, leaving a *positive mantissa* which remains the same whenever the number's significant figures are the same. But to write log 0·498 as −1·6972 would be very confusing and to write it as 0·6972 − 1 would be awkward. Instead, we write the minus sign above the characteristic and log 0·498 becomes $\bar{1}$·6972. This is read as 'bar 1·6972'; $\overline{17}$·634 would be 'bar 17·634' and so on. Do not forget that $\bar{1}$·6972 is 0·6972 − 1.

With this notation log 0·0498 becomes $\bar{2}$·6972
log 0·004 98 becomes $\bar{3}$·6972, etc.

It is worth noticing that the negative characteristic is numerically one more than the number of zeros after the decimal point: it is the index of the power of 10 which will multiply the number when expressed in standard form.

Example 5. Use the tables to find the logs of 0·3419, 0·034 19 and 0·003 419.

The mantissa for the first three significant figures—341 —is 5328 and the proportional part is 11, so the mantissa for the four significant figures, from the tables, is 5339.

The characteristic of the log of 0·3419 is −1, since 0·3419 in standard form is 3·419 × 10^{-1}. Therefore, log 0·3419 = $\bar{1}$·5339. Similarly, log 0·034 19 = $\bar{2}$·5339 and log 0·003 419 = $\bar{3}$·5339.

Example 6. Find anti-log $\bar{3}$·7683.

From the anti-log tables we find that the significant figures of the number whose mantissa is 7683 are 5865.

As the characteristic is -3, the anti-log is $5{\cdot}865 \times 10^{-3}$, which is $0{\cdot}005\ 865$.

Because of this rather curious, if useful, way of writing the logs of numbers less than 1, we need to be very careful when operating with them. Look at the examples closely.

Example 7. Find the sum of the logs: $\bar{1}{\cdot}6754$, $\bar{3}{\cdot}4785$, $\bar{1}{\cdot}9647$ and $0{\cdot}3647$.

We arrange the numbers as for ordinary addition:

$$
\begin{array}{r}
\bar{1}{\cdot}6754 \\
\bar{3}{\cdot}4785 \\
\bar{1}{\cdot}9647 \\
0{\cdot}3647 \\
\hline
\bar{3}{\cdot}4833
\end{array}
$$

When we carry the 2 over from the addition of the mantissae it is, of course, like them and positive. So the addition of the characteristics becomes

$$-1 - 3 - 1 + 0 + 2 = -3.$$

And so the sum is $-3 + 0{\cdot}4833$.

Example 8. Subtract the log $\bar{2}{\cdot}4765$ from the log $\bar{1}{\cdot}2863$.

$$
\begin{array}{r}
\bar{1}{\cdot}2863 \\
\bar{2}{\cdot}4765 \\
\hline
0{\cdot}8098
\end{array}
$$

Here we perform the operation as usual with the mantissa, and we find that we have had to 'borrow' 1 from the characteristic in order to subtract the 4 from the 2. The subtraction of the characteristics then becomes

$$-1 - (-2 + 1) = -1 + 2 - 1 = 0.$$

Example 9. Multiply $\bar{2}\cdot8421$ by 3.

$$\begin{array}{r} \bar{2}\cdot8421 \\ 3 \\ \hline \bar{4}\cdot5263 \end{array}$$

From the multiplication of the mantissa, 2 is carried forward. But this is positive and as $(-2) \times 3 = -6$, the characteristic becomes $-6 + 2 = -4$.

Example 10. Multiply $\bar{1}\cdot6362$ by $1\cdot6$.

In a case of this kind it is better to multiply the characteristic and mantissa separately and add the results.

Thus $\qquad 0\cdot6362 \times 1\cdot6 = \quad 1\cdot017\,92$
$$-1\cdot0 \times 1\cdot6 = -1\cdot6.$$

$-1\cdot6$ is wholly negative, so we change it to $\bar{2}\cdot4$ to make the mantissa positive; then the product is

$$1\cdot017\,92 + \bar{2}\cdot4$$
$$= \bar{1}\cdot417\,92,$$
$$\text{or } \bar{1}\cdot\bar{4}179 \text{ approximately.}$$

Example 11. Divide $\bar{2}\cdot3719$ by 3.

Here the difficulty is that 3 will not go into $\bar{2}$ exactly. In order to bypass the difficulty, we write $\bar{2}$ as $(-3 + 1)$ and the log as $-3 + 1\cdot3719$.

Then the division of -3 by 3 gives us -1, and the division of the positive part $1\cdot3719$ by 3 gives us $0\cdot4573$, which is positive. The complete quotient is therefore $\bar{1}\cdot4573$.

The work might be arranged as

$$3)\overline{\bar{3} + 1\cdot3719}$$
$$\bar{1} + 0\cdot4573$$
$$= \bar{1}\cdot4573$$

EXERCISE 23

1. Add together the following logarithms:

    (1) $\bar{3}\cdot7469 + \bar{2}\cdot6493 + 0\cdot0648 + 3\cdot3434$.
    (2) $\bar{2}\cdot6583 + 7\cdot8321 + 2\cdot6458 + \bar{1}\cdot2648$.

2. Find the value of:

    (1) $4\cdot3872 - 5\cdot9374$.
    (2) $0\cdot3874 - \bar{1}\cdot2549$.
    (3) $\bar{1}\cdot6538 - \bar{1}\cdot5738$.
    (4) $\bar{3}\cdot8764 - \bar{5}\cdot3982$.

3. Find the value of:

    (1) $\bar{1}\cdot2864 \times 2$.
    (2) $\bar{2}\cdot8742 \times 3$.
    (3) $\bar{1}\cdot8391 \times 6$.
    (4) $\bar{1}\cdot7825 \times 1\cdot5$.
    (5) $\bar{2}\cdot4793 \times 0\cdot3$.
    (6) $\bar{2}\cdot1756 \times 0\cdot5$.

4. Find the value of:

    (1) $\bar{3}\cdot9878 \times 0\cdot45$.
    (2) $\bar{2}\cdot4593 \times 0\cdot76$.
    (3) $2\cdot4123 \times -0\cdot2$.
    (4) $\bar{1}\cdot6431 \times -0\cdot8$.

5. Find the value of:

    (1) $\bar{1}\cdot4879 \div 2$.
    (2) $\bar{2}\cdot7653 \div 5$.
    (3) $\bar{4}\cdot8173 \div 3$.
    (4) $\bar{3}\cdot1951 \div 1\cdot6$.
    (5) $\bar{1}\cdot6296 \div 0\cdot8$.

6. If $A = mn^{1\cdot6}$, find A when $m = 2\cdot35$ and $n = 3\cdot78$.

7. If $A = P\left(1 + \dfrac{r}{100}\right)^n$, what is A when $P = 2350$, $r = 6\cdot4$, $n = 3\frac{3}{4}$?

8. If $V = \frac{4}{3}\pi r^3$, what is r when $V = 500$?

CHAPTER 13

Standard Measures

In order to measure amounts of things, we need not only to be able to count them but also to count them in a way that can readily be understood by others. We may, for example, say that we have two cakes or three apples, but this tells us little about the amount of cake or apple we have: they may be small cakes or they may be huge.

Unless potatoes were all the same size, we would be shy of buying potatoes at 1p each unless we knew how big each potato was. Similarly, we would want to know how big the cans of petrol were if they sold at 10p each—if they were large cans they might be a bargain.

If A has 3 cans of petrol and B has 2 cans, who has more petrol? Without knowing the size of the cans we are in no position to judge.

Farmer Giles has 2 fields but Mr Archer has 4: who owns more land? Again we cannot tell without knowing how big the fields are.

We need *standard* sizes. We all know that potatoes are bought by weight, petrol by liquid capacity and fields by area. What we are actually doing is comparing the weight of our potatoes with a standard weight, the amount of our petrol with a standard amount of liquid and the area of our fields with a standard area. These standard quantities are our basic *units of measurement*.

Units—so-called because of the Latin word for 'one'— are standard quantities, of which our amount is a multiple. For example, when we talk of £5 we mean

5 × £1 and £1 is the unit. Clearly, units need not merely be one of something. £5 is also 5 × £1, where 100p is the unit; on the other hand, 500p is 500 × 1p, where 1p is the unit.

There is no difficulty in the idea of a unit; we all use units every day when we talk of quantities of money, distance, weight, speed, etc. The important thing to establish first is that we all have the same meaning for a unit.

The Egyptians were among the first to try to introduce units: they used, for example, the cubit, which was the length of a man's forearm. Useful though this was, and an advance on previous measuring arrangements, the lengths of men's forearms differed as much then as they do now and the cubit could never be more than a rough measure. In England, Henry VIII made the next move by nominating the basic unit of length, the foot, not as any man's foot but specifically as his own. All the other traditional British (or Imperial) units were defined in a similarly haphazard way.

But now Britain is changing most of its units, and its units of currency have already changed. There are two reasons for this change.

In these cosmopolitan days it is not enough for people of one country to understand each other: anyone used to dealing in Imperial units who has asked a distance abroad, or tried to buy butter or petrol, will know the problem. Now we must all speak the same measuring-language. Secondly, Imperial units often involved you in complicated sums simply because there were 3 feet to a yard, 8 pints to a gallon or whatever. By changing to a decimal system (a system which counts in tens and not in threes or eights) complicated arithmetic is considerably reduced. Now we will measure everything (with one notable exception) in tens and life will be much simpler. The notable exception is, of course, time. We will doubtless continue to use the year and day as being convenient mirrors of nature, and all the units as being universally accepted.

It needs little effort to grasp the basic elements of the metric system, but only practice and familiarity will make them mean something in terms of everyday notions like the length of your stride.

The metric units of length and mass are the metre and the gramme; other units of length and mass which are used in the metric system are constructed by the combination of the metre and the gramme with prefixes (see Table I below) which have the same effect—of multiplying or dividing—when combined with other metric units. For example, the kilogramme is 1000 grammes, the kilometre is 1000 metres and the kilowatt is 1000 watts.

It is probably worth mentioning weight and mass at this point. Technically, they are different things measured in different units, but they are, unfortunately, often confused. The mass of something is constant *wherever it is*: it is this quantity people try to reduce by slimming. The weight of a body is a force, the force it exerts because of the effect of gravity on its mass. Even though going into space makes people weightless, the experience is hardly a good substitute for a suitable diet. But it is only recently that people have begun to go into space, and our weight on earth is pretty much the same wherever we are (there are slight variations but nothing which need worry us here). Since weights were measured against 'weights' of a pound mass of iron, it was natural to refer to our weights in pounds, although strictly we should have said pounds-force. Now, as has been said, the metric unit of mass is the gramme; the metric unit of

Table I. Standard metric prefixes (see text)

Prefix	Abbreviation	Value (multiply by)	Example
tera	T	10^{12}	1 Tm = 1 terameter = 1 000 000 000 000 m.
giga	G	10^{9}	1 Gg = 1 gigagramme = 1 000 000 000 g.
mega	M	10^{6}	1 MW = 1 megawatt = 1 000 000 W.
kilo	k	10^{3}	1 kg = 1 kilogramme or kilo = 1000 g.
*hecto	h	10^{2}	1 ha = 1 hectare = 100 a.
*centi	c	10^{-2}	1 cm = 1 centimetre = 1/100 m.
milli	m	10^{-3}	1 ml = 1 millilitre = 1/1000 l.
micro	μ †	10^{-6}	1μs = 1 microsecond = 1/1 000 000 s.
nano	n	10^{-9}	1 nV = 1 nanovolt = 1/1 000 000 000 V.
pico	p	10^{-12}	1 pF = 1 picofarad = 1/1 000 000 000 000 F.

* cm and ha are the only measures which normally take these prefixes; in principle they are not allowed because they are not multiples of 1000, but they are admitted for convenience.

† 'μ' is the small Greek letter 'mu'.

force based on the kilogramme is the newton (after Sir Isaac Newton) and it is the force needed to increase the speed of a mass of 1 kilogramme by 1 metre per second in a second. That may seem quite complicated (although it is elementary physics), but we also use a unit called the kilogramme-force (kgf), which is the force exerted by 1 kg on earth. However, the newton (N) is most convenient for most occasions.

In this book mass and weight are always differentiated, and you should make the distinction too.

Now, apart from mass and length, there will still be the old units of time (which, except when we are making seconds smaller, do not use the metric prefixes) and then there are a host of other units which are derived from the basic units: some of these have completely different names. Some are shown in Table II. These measures which do have different names combine normally with the prefixes of Table I. Units made by combining two or more basic units do not use the prefixes: prefixes used with such combined units apply only to the measure

Table II. Metric units.

(Units marked with an asterisk (*) cannot be combined with the prefixes of Table 1.)

Quantity measured	Name of unit	Abbreviation
length/distance	metre	m
mass	gramme (*=1 cm^3 of water at 4°C*)	g
	tonne = 1 Mg	t
time	second	s
	minute = 60 s	*min
	hour = 60 min	*h
speed	metre per second	m/s *or* ms^{-1}
	kilometre per hour	*km/h *or* kmh^{-1}
acceleration	metre per second per second *or* metre per second squared	m/s^2 *or* ms^{-2}
area	square metre *or* metre squared	*m^2
	are = 100 m^2	a
volume/cubic capacity	cubic metre *or* metre cubed	*m^3
liquid capacity	litre (*=100 cm^3 of water at 4°C*)	l
force	newton = 1 kg m/s^2	N
	kilogramme-force = 9·81 kg ms/^{2}	*kgf
work	joule = 1 Nm = 1 kg m^2/s^2	J
power	watt = 1 J/s = 1 kg m^2/s^3	W
†temperature	celsius degree	*C°
change	absolute degree	*A°

† In fact, 1 absolute degree and 1 celsius degree are equal and represent a *change* in temperature. 1 degree centigrade (1°C) does *not* equal 1 degree absolute (1°A) since these are temperatures. 1°C = 274°A. 0°C is the freezing point and 100°C the boiling point of water. Notice that there is no full point after the abbreviations, which remain unaltered in the plural: m is the abbreviation for metre *and* metres, ms for metre-second.

immediately after the prefix, not to the whole unit. So, for example, $1 \text{ mm}^3 = 1 \text{ mm} \times \text{mm} \times \text{mm}$, *not* $\frac{1}{1000}$ m³.

Finally, the prefixes cannot be added to units that are already prefixed: 1 mkm (meaning 1 metre) is not allowed.

The unit of area is the *square metre* (m²): the area of a square measuring 1 m along each side.

If this square is divided 1000 times along one side and then 1000 times along an adjacent side, each division along the two sides will be 1 mm long. If we draw straight lines through each of the divisions and parallel to the sides of the square, we will have drawn 10^6 ($=10^3 \times 10^3$) small squares, each of which is a *square millimetre* (mm²). So, $1 \text{ m}^2 = 1\,000\,000 \text{ mm}^2$. Similarly, $1 \text{ km}^2 = 1\,000\,000$ m².

The unit of volume is the *cubic metre* (m³): the volume of a cube measuring 1 m along each side.

Dividing the cube into smaller cubes each 1 mm × 1 mm × 1 mm, you will be able to see, gives us 10^9 ($=10^3 \times 10^3 \times 10^3$) small cubes, each of which is 1 *cubic millimetre* (mm³). So, $1 \text{ m}^3 = 10^9 \text{ mm}^2$. This is what you should expect, since $1 \text{ m}^2 = 1 \text{ m} \times 1 \text{ m} = 10^3 \text{ mm} \times 10^3 \text{ mm} = 10^6 \text{ mm}^2$, etc.

For further consideration of area and volume, see chapters 20–22.

There are a number of common metric units that have not been included in Table II: the centimetre is an example. And all the derived units (for work and so on) are based on the kilogramme, not the gramme. The reason is that there are several variant versions of the metric system.

One—the one commonly used until recently—took the centimetre, the gramme and the second as basic units (the cgs system) compared with the British foot–pound-

second (fps) system. But it has been found that the
metre, kilogramme and second form a more convenient
basis for measurement. This is the mks system and it is
the system being adopted—at various speeds—by all
countries: it is the *Système Internationale* or SI.

One of the features of SI is that it excludes prefixes
which are not multiples of 1000; in particular, it excludes
the prefix centi- and thus the centimetre as an SI unit.
In practice, however, the centimetre is likely to continue
in use.

There is another class of units which has been excluded

Table III. Relation of Imperial (British) units to metric units

	linear		
1 m	1·093 614 yards	1 yd	0·914 399 m
1 mm	0·089 370 inches	1 inch	25·399 98 mm
1 km	0·621 372 miles	1 mile	1·609 343 km
	area		
1 m^2	10·763 87 sq. ft	1 sq. ft	0·092 90 m^2
1 m^2	1·195 99 sq. yd	1 sq. yd	0·863 13 m^2
1 km^2	0·386 10 sq. miles	1 sq. mile	2·590 00 km^2
	volume		
1 a	0·024 71 acres	1 acre	40·469 a
1 m^3	35·314 45 cu. ft	1 cu. ft	0·028 32 m^3
1 m^3	1·307 94 cu. yd	1 cu. yd	0·764 56 m^3
	capacity		
1 l	1·760 72 pt	1 pt	0·567 95 l
1 l	0·220 09 gal	1 gal	4·543 60 l
	mass		
1 g	0·035 270 oz	1 oz	28·349 530 g
1 kg	2·204 620 lb	1 lb	0·453 592 kg
1 t	0·984 tons	1 ton	1·016 047 t

Note: By the Weights and Measures Act 1963, the yard and the pound
are *defined* by reference to the International Metre and Kilogramme:
the yard as 0·9144 m exactly and the pound as 0·453 592 37 kg
exactly. The metre is defined by reference to the wavelength of light
and the kilogramme by reference to the properties of atoms.

from Table II, although the units are permitted in SI: they are units like km², km/s², which are units formed directly from mks units and which cannot be modified by the addition of prefixes from Table I.

It is assumed that readers have sufficient knowledge of the Imperial units for them to be happily excluded here, but Table III shows the relation of some Imperial units to metric units.

You may have noticed that longer numbers (those of more than three digits on one or both sides of the decimal point) are not divided by commas, as they used to be. Instead, numbers are divided up into groups of three, *counting away from the decimal point in each direction*. These groups are separated by spaces. They are divided simply to make them easier to read—short numbers of four or five digits may not be divided at all—and this used to be done with the comma: but in some countries the comma is used as the decimal point. The number 1046793·96842155 can be written as it is, as 1 046 793·968 421 55 or as 1 046 793,968 421 55.

Money

Since 15 February, 1971, the British system of currency has been decimal. Indeed, it was expected that it might take up to or over 18 months to dispose of *s* and *d*, but within 12 months they had been forgotten almost completely.

Now, £1 (one pound) = 100p (pence).

By having one basic unit divided into 100 sub-units, Britain is brought into line with almost every other country in the world, although some still retain 20 shillings to the local pound.

Now there is talk of the £ sterling being abolished, along with all the other existing Common Market currencies, and replaced with a single European currency. This would probably be the Eurodollar (€). But if this happens, our problems will not be arithmetical: all problems involving €s will be identical to those involving £s: only the names will be changed, and, of course, the values.

The relation between British and Foreign units of currency fluctuates.

Example 1. What is the sum, in metres, of the following quantities: 3462 cm, 854 mm, 923 mm, 845 cm, 5643 mm?

$$
\begin{aligned}
\text{Since} \qquad 1 \text{ cm} &= 1 \text{ m} \div 10^2, \\
3642 \text{ cm} &= (3462 \div 10^2) \text{ m} = 34{\cdot}62 \text{ m}; \\
\text{similarly,} \quad 854 \text{ mm} &= (854 \div 10^3) \text{ m} = 0{\cdot}854 \text{ m} \\
923 \text{ mm} &= (923 \div 10^3) \text{ m} = 0{\cdot}923 \text{ m} \\
845 \text{ cm} &= (845 \div 10^2) \text{ m} = 8{\cdot}45 \text{ m} \\
5643 \text{ mm} &= (5643 \div 10^3) \text{ m} = 5{\cdot}643 \text{ m} \\
\therefore \text{ total} \qquad &= 50{\cdot}490 \text{ m}.
\end{aligned}
$$

Example 2. How many pieces of string can be cut from a length 75·6 m long if each piece is to be 35 cm long?

(1) $\qquad\qquad 75{\cdot}6 \text{ m} = 7560 \text{ cm}$
$\qquad \therefore \text{ number of pieces} = 7560 \div 35$
$\qquad\qquad\qquad\qquad\qquad = 216.$

(2) $\qquad \text{number of pieces} = \dfrac{75{\cdot}6 \text{ m}}{35 \text{ cm}}$
$\qquad\qquad\qquad\qquad\qquad = 2{\cdot}16 \times 100$
$\qquad\qquad\qquad\qquad\qquad = 216.$

Example 3. What is the sum in m² of: 3256 m², 6143 cm², 39·8 a? And what is the sum in ares?

$$3256 \text{ m}^2 = 3\ 256 \text{ m}^2$$
$$6143 \text{ cm}^2 = 6143 \div 10^4 \text{ m}^2 = 0.6143 \text{ m}^2$$
$$39.8 \text{ a} = 39.8 \times 10^2 \text{ m}^2 = 3980 \text{ m}^2$$
$$\therefore \text{ total} = 7236.6143 \text{ m}^2.$$

$$7236.6143 \text{ m}^2 = (7236.6143 \div 100) \text{ a} = 72.366\ 143 \text{ a}.$$

Example 4. 60 books cost 14 000 Belgian francs. What is the unit cost in sterling ($£1 = 115$ B fr)?

$$60 \text{ cost } 14\ 000 \text{ B fr}$$

$$\therefore 1 \text{ costs } \frac{14\ 000}{60} \text{ B fr}$$

$$\therefore 1 \text{ costs } £\frac{14\ 000}{60 \times 115}$$

$$= \frac{£140}{69}$$

$$= £2.03 \text{ (to the nearest penny)}.$$

EXERCISE 24

1. Express in metres and add: 326 cm, 48 056 mm, 4278 cm.
2. Express in kilometres and add: 8245 cm, 924 km, 84 365 mm, 2356 cm, 84 573 mm.
3. Multiply 8·915 m by 13 km. What sort of quantity does the answer represent?
4. How many pieces of card 3 mm thick are there in a pile 1·5 mm high?
5. What is the height in (1) metres, (2) kilometres of a mountain 14 501 ft high?
6. Find the length in miles of a journey of 872 km.
7. How many square metres are there in 100 a?
8. If 40 lb of gunk cost £1·34, what is the cost in fr/kg ($£1 = 13·15$ francs)?

CHAPTER 14

Simple Equations and Problems

Equations

In every arithmetical problem our object is to find the value of some unknown quantity from the known values of certain other quantities. And all the fundamental operations of addition, subtraction, etc., are of practical use only insofar as they help us to find this unknown quantity. In algebra it is the same. Certain conditions are given us, and the relation between these conditions, and from this information we frame what is called an *equation* or an equality; and, by means of the processes of addition, subtraction, multiplication and division, we find the unknown quantity of which we are in search. For example, in the formula $\frac{1}{2}mv^2 = Fs$ we have given that half of the mass $\times$ the square of the velocity $=$ the force $\times$ the space through which the force acts. This is an equation or an equality between two quantities. Suppose now that v is the unknown quantity in the above equation, and that $m = 8$, $F = 135$, $s = 10$. Then the equation becomes

$$\frac{1}{2} \times 8 \times v^2 = 135 \times 10$$
$$\therefore \quad 4v^2 = 1350$$
$$\therefore \quad v^2 = 337\cdot5$$
$$\therefore \quad v = \sqrt{337\cdot5}$$
$$= 18\cdot37.$$

In finding the value of the unknown quantity v, or in what is called *solving the equation*, we divided each side of the equation $4v^2 = 1350$ by 4, relying on the self-evident truth that when equal quantities are divided by the same quantity the quotients are equal. Similarly, in the next equation, $v^2 = 3375$, we rely on the fact that the square roots of equal quantities are equal.

The axioms, or self-evident truths on which we rely in solving equations, may be summed up as follows:

1. **Axiom of addition.** If equal quantities be added to each side of an equation, the sums are equal.

2. **Axiom of subtraction.** If equal quantities be subtracted from each side of an equation, the remainders are equal.

3. **Axiom of multiplication.** If each side of an equation be multiplied by equal quantities, the products are equal.

4. **Axiom of division.** If each side of an equation be divided by equal quantities, the quotients are equal.

Also, the two sides will still be equal when the square root, cube root, etc., of each side is taken.

These axioms are true of both arithmetical and algebraical quantities.

Let us see how they apply in the following example:

$$3x - 2 = 5x - 7.$$

Here the unknown x appears on both sides of the equation. Known numbers also appear on both sides. But we want the unknown numbers to appear on one side and the known on the other side, for we want to be able to say that $x =$ some known number. Now, applying the axiom of subtraction, we can get rid of $5x$ on the right-hand side by *subtracting* $5x$ from both sides, which makes the equation:

$$3x - 5x - 2 = 5x - 5x - 7,$$
or $\qquad 3x - 5x - 2 = -7.$

Similarly, to get rid of -2 on the left-hand side we *add* 2 to both sides, which makes the equation:

$$3x - 5x - 2 + 2 = -7 + 2,$$
or $\qquad 3x - 5x = -7 + 2.$

But a little consideration will show that this process is the same thing as if we were to *transpose* the quantities from one side to the other and *change their signs*. Thus:

$$3x - 2 = 5x - 7$$
becomes $3x - 5x = -7 + 2.$

Hence the convenient rule (*which, however, is meaningless apart from the above explanation*): Transpose all the terms containing the unknown quantity to one side, and all the known quantities to the other, *changing the signs of all the transposed terms*.

Example 1.

$$2x - x - 4 + 7 = 3x - 6 + 10$$
$$2x - x - 3x = -6 + 10 - 7 + 4$$
$$-2x = +1$$

$\therefore$ (dividing by -2) $x = \dfrac{1}{-2} = -\dfrac{1}{2}.$

Example 2.

$$15(x - 1) + 4(x + 3) = 2(7 + x)$$
$\therefore \ 15x - 15 + 4x + 12 = 14 + 2x$
$\therefore \ 15x + 4x - 2x \qquad = 14 - 12 + 15$ (by axioms 1
$\qquad\qquad\qquad\qquad\qquad\qquad$ and 2)

$\therefore \qquad\qquad 17x \quad = 17$
$\therefore \qquad\qquad\quad x \quad = 1 \qquad\qquad$ (by axiom 4).

Example 3. Example of a *fractional* equation:

$$\frac{x + 5}{6} + \frac{x + 1}{9} = \frac{x + 3}{4}.$$

Here we first get rid of the fractional form by multiplying each side by *such a quantity as will cause* 6, 9 *and* 4 *to disappear*. Now, the *multiplier* of each side which will cause 6, 9 and 4 to disappear will be a *common multiple* of 6, 9 and 4. And it will be convenient to get the *lowest* common multiple. This is 36.

Accordingly, when we multiply each side by 36 we get:

$$36\frac{(x+5)}{6} + 36\frac{(x+1)}{9} = 36\frac{(x+3)}{4},$$

or $6(x+5) + 4(x+1) = 9(x+3),$

or $6x + 30 + 4x + 4 = 9x + 27,$

$\therefore 10x - 9x = 27 - 34$

$x = -7.$

EXERCISE 25

Solve the following equations:

1. $2x - 3 = -4x - 9.$
2. $x - 4 = 9 - 2x.$
3. $x^2 - 5 = x^2 - x.$
4. $2x - 3 - 5x = 8 - x.$
5. $p - 6 + 2p = 3 - p.$
6. $\dfrac{x+1}{2} - \dfrac{x-1}{3} = 6.$
7. $\dfrac{5x}{2} + \dfrac{3x}{4} = \dfrac{x}{2} + 1.$
8. $\dfrac{x-1}{3} - \dfrac{x-2}{4} = \dfrac{x-3}{5}.$
9. $\dfrac{2x}{3} + \dfrac{x}{5} - \dfrac{3x}{7} = 18.$
10. $\dfrac{2(x+1)}{7} - \dfrac{3(x+2)}{8} = \dfrac{x}{2}.$
11. $\frac{1}{4}(x+3) - \frac{1}{3}(2x+1) = 3x.$ [*First step:* $3(x+3) - 4(2x+1) = 36x.$]
12. $\frac{2}{3}(x+5) + \frac{3}{4}(x+7) = 3(x-1).$
13. $\dfrac{x}{2} + \dfrac{x}{3} - \dfrac{x}{4} + \dfrac{x}{5} = 14.$
14. $0.5x - \frac{2}{3}x - 0.5 = 4\frac{1}{2}.$ [*First step:* $\frac{1}{2}x - \frac{2}{3}x - \frac{1}{2} = \frac{9}{2}.$]
15. $0.15x - 2x + 0.75 = 0.3 + 2\frac{1}{2} - x.$

16. Find the value of A in the equation $A = \frac{1}{2}hb$, when $h = 12$ and $b = 11$.

17. Find the value of V in the equation $V = \frac{1}{3}a^2h$, when $a = 16$ and $h = 20$.

18. Find the value of s in the equation $s = \frac{1}{2}gt^2$, when $g = 32 \cdot 2$ and $t = 7$.

19. Find the value of s in the equation $\frac{1}{2}mv^2 = Fs$, when $m = 7$, $F = 110$, $v = 8$.

20. Find the value of a in the equation $v^2 - u^2 = 2as$, when $v = 50$, $u = 12$, $s = 100$.

21. In the formula $F = \dfrac{mv^2}{gr}$ find m when $F = 120$, $v = 40$, $g = 32$ and $r = 4$.

22. In the equation $v^2 = 2fs$ find the value of v when $s = 300$ and $f = 2\frac{1}{2}$.

23. In the equation $\dfrac{w}{w - 300} = \dfrac{13}{2}$ find the value of w.

24. In the equation $s = Vt + \frac{1}{2}ft^2$ find the value of V when $s = 120$, $t = 1$, $f = 32$.

25. In the equation of the previous exercise find the value of f when $s = 8000$, $V = 20$ and $t = 50$.

26. In the formula $I = \dfrac{PNR}{100}$ find the value of I when $P = 400$, $N = 3$, $R = 2\frac{1}{2}$.

27. In the formula $P = \dfrac{100\,I}{NR}$ find the value of P when $I = 60$, $N = 2$, $R = 3\frac{1}{2}$.

28. In the formula $N = \dfrac{100\,I}{PR}$ find the value of N when $I = £6 \cdot 87\frac{1}{2}$, $P = £320$, and $R = 2\frac{1}{2}$.

29. In the formula $R = \dfrac{100\,I}{PN}$ find the value of R when $I = £60$, $P = £1015$, $N = 2\frac{1}{2}$.

30. In the formula $A = 2h(l + b)$ find the value of:
    (1) A when $h = 15$, $l = 25$, $b = 15$;
    (2) h when $A = 405$, $l = 10$, $b = 8$.

Solution of problems by equations

Nearly every question in applied science resolves itself into the solution of an equation. Thus, in the case of a body falling vertically from rest, the relation between the space described and the time of falling is expressed in the formula $s = \frac{1}{2}gt^2$, where s denotes the space described, t the time in seconds and $g = 9 \cdot 81$ m/s² (i.e. the acceleration of a body falling freely). Now, suppose we want to find the depth of a well which we cannot conveniently measure directly. In the law $s = \frac{1}{2}gt^2$ we can easily find t by dropping a stone to the bottom and counting the time in seconds. Suppose the time is 2 s. Then

$$s = \frac{1}{2} \times 9\cdot81 \times 2^2$$
$$= \frac{1}{2} \times 9\cdot81 \times 4$$
$$= 19\cdot62 \text{ m.}$$

But, besides their value in applied science, equations are often of considerable service in solving arithmetical problems that present some difficulty.

Example 4. How much tea at 60p a kilogramme must be mixed with 5 kg of tea at 50p per kg, so that the mixture may be worth 55p per kg?

Let x be the required number of kg of tea at 60p per kg; then we are given that the price of x kg at 60p + price of 5 kg at 50p = price of $(x + 5)$ kg at 55p.

$60 \times x$ pence + 5×50 pence = $(x + 5) \times 55$ pence
i.e. $60x + 250 = 55x + 275$
$\therefore$ $5x = 25$
$\therefore$ $x = 5$

$\therefore$ 5 kg of tea at 60p per kg must be bought.

Example 5. A merchant mixes 35 litres of petrol at 33p per litre with 42 litres of petrol at 39p. What is the minimum price at which he can sell the mixture so as to gain at least 10%?

Let x be the selling price in pence per litre. From our information, we have:

$$35 \times 33 + 42 \times 39 = (35 + 42)x - 10/100 \text{ of total}$$
$$\text{cost of petrol.}$$

i.e. $\quad 1155 + 1638 = 77x - 1/10(1155 + 1638)$

$\therefore \qquad\qquad 2793 = 77x - 279 \cdot 3$

$\therefore \qquad\qquad 77x = 2793 + 279 \cdot 3$

$$x = 39 \cdot 9$$

$\therefore$ selling price should be 40p per litre.

The chief difficulty the beginner in algebra has with equations is not the mere solution but the *forming of the equation (or equations) from the given conditions*. And this difficulty often arises from the difficulty of expressing the conditions in symbols. Thus, if a man walks 40 km at the rate of 4 km an hour, it is easy to tell the time he takes. But when the same sort of problem is expressed in symbolical language—'If a man walks a km at the rate of b km per hour, how many hours does he take?'—it is not quite so familiar. Yet, until the student can do this sort of thing quite readily, he is handicapped in all equational work involving problems. Further, an intelligent knowledge of the various formulae of practical science depends on the proper understanding of symbolical expressions, for all formulae are symbolical.

The following are examples of what the student should be able to do in the way of making symbolical expressions:

Example 6. If T = time in hours,
$\qquad\qquad$ D = distance in km,
$\qquad\qquad$ R = rate in km per hour.

To express each in terms of the others:

$$T = \frac{D}{R}, \quad D = TR, \quad R = \frac{D}{T}.$$

Example 7. If a man walks y km in x days, what is his rate per day?

$$R = \frac{D}{T}$$
$$= \frac{y}{x} \text{ km per day.}$$

Example 8. What is the speed in metres per second of a train which travels 95 km in x hours?

$$R = \frac{D}{T}$$
$$= \frac{95}{x} \text{ km/h}$$
$$= \left(\frac{95}{x} \div 3600\right) \text{ km/s}$$
$$= \frac{95}{3600x} \text{ km/s}$$
$$= \frac{19}{720x} \text{ km/s}$$
$$= \left(\frac{19}{720x} \times 1000\right) \text{ m/s}$$
$$= 26\cdot4 \text{ m/s.}$$

Example 9. If I spend $4x$ pence a week, how many pounds do I save out of a yearly income of £y?

$$\text{Money spent in a year} = 52 \times 4x \text{ pence}$$
$$= \frac{208x}{100} \text{ pounds}$$
$$\therefore \text{ money saved} = £(y - 2\cdot08x).$$

Example 10. How long will it take a person to walk p km if he walks 30 km in q hours?

$$\text{Rate} = \frac{30}{q}$$

$$\text{and } T = \frac{D}{R}$$

$$= \frac{p}{\frac{30}{q}} = \frac{pq}{30}.$$

EXERCISE 26

1. If the sum of two numbers be 72, and one of them is p, what is the other?

2. If the sum of two numbers be p, and one of them is q, what is the other number?

3. How many hours will it take to walk p km at $3\frac{1}{2}$ km an hour?

4. A train goes x km an hour; how long will it take to go 350 km?

5. A man buys m items at $\frac{1}{2}$p each and n at 50p each. How much has he spent, in pounds?

6. Find the value in pence of x pounds and y pence.

7. How long will it take to fill a tank which holds b litres if it fills at the rate of c litres per hour?

8. If a man walks k km in q hours, what is his rate of walking?

9. What is the mass in tonnes of 320 balls if 20 have mass z kg?

10. What is the distance between two places if a train travelling p km an hour takes 6 hours to do the journey?

EXERCISE 27

1. Divide a line 16 cm long into two parts such that the length of one is 3 times the length of the other.

2. Divide £1000 between two men so that one may get 4 times as much as the other.

3. A post has $\frac{1}{4}$ of its length in the mud, $\frac{1}{3}$ in the water and 12 m of it visible above water. What is the total length of the post?

4. A sum of £11·35 is made up of 74 coins, some of which are worth 50p and the rest 5p; how many of each coin are there? (*Note*: this calls for an equation in which the equality must be: value of 50's + value of 5's = £11·35.)

5. Divide £350 between A, B and C so that B and C may each get $\frac{1}{3}$ of what A gets.

6. How much tea at 75p a kilo must be mixed with 20 kilo at 60p each so as to make the mixture worth 65p a kilo? (A *kilo* is the usual name for a kilogramme.)

7. Divide £60 between A, B and C so that A has £8 more than B and B £2 more than C.

8. A friend, walking at the rate of 3 km an hour, starts 2 hours before me. When should I be able to overtake him walking at the rate of 4 km an hour?

(*Note :* The friend walks $(2 + x)$ hours; and since the *distance* travelled by both will be the same, the equation will be friend's time × rate = my time × rate; for time × rate = distance.)

CHAPTER 15

Simultaneous Equations

The meaning and utility of a pair of simultaneous equations may be explained as follows:

In connection with mechanical appliances certain things are found to vary with one another. As one thing increases another may decrease. Thus, the pressure and volume of a given quantity of gas vary in such a way that the greater the pressure becomes, the less the volume becomes. In the case of a machine two forces may be operative, one called the *effort* (E) and the other the *resistance* (R), and it is found that these two forces vary. Now, by experiments it is found out how these forces vary, and the knowledge thus gained is called the *Law of the Machine*. Such laws are of practical value in determining such problems as the kind of machine necessary to do a certain amount of work—it may be lifting some weight. Now, suppose the law of a machine is expressed in the *formula*

$$E = aR + b,$$

where *a* and *b* are constants, and it is found that when E is 16, R is 6; and when E is 40, R is 12. How are we to make the formula give us a *numerical* result which will be of *practical guidance* in the making of the machine?

If we take the first values of E and R the formula becomes

$$16 = 6a + b.$$

If we take the second values of E and R the formula becomes

$$40 = 12a + b.$$

Here, then, from two equations we have to find the values of two unknowns—a and b. We proceed as follows:

(1) $\quad 6a + b = 16.$
(2) $\quad 12a + b = 40.$

Multiply (1) by 2 and we get (according to the axiom)

(3) $\quad 12a + 2b = 32.$

Now subtract (3) from (2) and we get

$$-b = 8,$$
or $\quad b = -8.$

Substitute the value of b in equation (1) and we get

$$6a - 8 = 16;$$
$$\therefore \quad 6a = 24,$$
$$\therefore \quad a = 4.$$
$$\text{Now} \quad E = a\text{R} + b.$$
$$\therefore \quad E = 4\text{R} - 8.$$

This result shows what must be the relation between the *effort* of the machine and the *resistance* it has to overcome.

From the fact that two (or more) equations are given in connection with the *same* problem, the equations are called *simultaneous*; and their solution is found by adding, subtracting, multiplying or dividing in accordance with the axioms given above.

We add other examples of how to solve simultaneous equations.

Example 1.   (1) $2p + q = 50$.
                   (2) $7p - 3q = 14$.

Multiply (1) by 3 and it becomes

$$(3)\ 6p + 3q = 150.$$

Add (3) and (2) and we get

$$(4)\ 13p = 164,$$
$$\therefore\quad p = 12\tfrac{8}{13}.$$

Substitute the value of p in (1) thus:

$$25\tfrac{3}{13} + q = 50.$$
$$\therefore q = 50 - 25\tfrac{3}{13}$$
$$= 24\tfrac{10}{13}.$$

Example 2. If, when A is 3, B is 1, and when A is 8, B is 6, find the values of a and b in the equation A = aB + b.

From what is given, we get the following simultaneous equations:

$$(1)\ 3 = a + b.$$
$$(2)\ 8 = 6a + b.$$

Subtracting (2) from (1) we get

$$-5\ = -5a.$$
$$\text{or } -5a = -5.$$
$$\therefore\quad a = 1.$$

Substituting the value of a in (1) we get

$$3 = 1 + b,$$
$$\therefore b = 2.$$

Example 3. A builder wishes to mix sand at 75p per kg with another sort at 90p per kg in such a way as to make 60 kg worth 80p per kg. What quantity of each sort must he take?

Let x = number of kg at 75p
and y =   ,,   ,,   90p.
Then the value of x kg = $75x$p
and   ,,   ,, y kg = $90y$p.

The conditions give:

$$x \text{ kg} + y \text{ kg} = 60 \text{ kg}$$
and $$75x\text{p} + 90y\text{p} = (60 \times 80)\text{p}.$$

Or, in simpler form:

(1) $x + y = 60$
(2) $75x + 90y = 4800.$

Dividing (2) by 15, and multiplying (1) by 5,

(1) gives (3) $5x + 5y = 300$
(2) gives (4) $5x + 6y = 320.$

Subtracting (3) from (4) we get $y = 20$, and substituting this value of y in (1) we get

$$x + 20 = 60$$
$$\therefore x = 40.$$

Answer: 40 kg at 75p and 20 kg at 90p.

(*Verification*—$40 \times 75\text{p} = £30$
$20 \times 90\text{p} = £18$
$\therefore$ 60 kg sells for $£48$
$\therefore$ 1 kg sells for $£0.80 = 80\text{p}$.)

Example 4. Solve the equations:

(1) $3x + 4y = 11.$
(2) $2x + 3y = 8.$

It will be seen from the preceding examples that our aim in multiplying either or both equations by some number is to get two equations in which the coefficients of x will be the same, or in which the coefficients of y will be the same. Suppose that we wish to get from the given equations two new equations in which the co-efficients of y will be the same, we shall clearly get two such equations if we multiply both sides of (1) by 3 and both sides of (2) by 4.

(1) gives $9x + 12y = 33$
(2) gives $8x + 12y = 32$

$\therefore$ by subtraction we get $x = 1.$

If we now substitute this value of x in (1) we get $y = 2.$

If we had wished to get two equations in which the co-efficients of x were the same we should have multiplied both sides of (1) by 2 and both sides of (2) by 3.

EXERCISE 28

Solve the following equations:

1. $x + y = 4.$
   $x - y = 2.$
2. $3x - y = 4.$
   $x + 2y = 6.$
3. $p - q = 2.$
   $2p - q = -3.$
4. $8x - y = 34.$
   $x + 8y = 53.$
5. $3x = 7y.$
   $12y - 5x = -1.$
6. $2A + B = 3.$
   $3B - A = 7.$
7. $B - A = 6.$
   $-3B - 2A = 9.$
8. If when $F = 100$, $B = 8$, and when F is 210, $B = 16$, find the value of F in the formula $F = aB + c$.

9. Half the sum of two numbers is 20, and three times their difference is 18; find the numbers.

10. 5 kg of tea and 4 kg of sugar cost £3·92; 8 kg of tea and 6 kg of sugar cost £6·24; find the cost of a kilo of each.

11. The wages of 10 men and 6 boys amount to £15. If 4 men together receive £2 more than 4 boys, what are the wages of a man and a boy?

12. If when E is 9, R is 24, and when E is 13, R is 37, find the values of a and b in the equation $E = aR + b$.

13. If when E is 72, W is 168, and when E is 90½, W is 220, what are the values of a and b in the equation $E = aW + b$?

NOTE

We have now given the reader an account of the basic ideas and the simplest uses of algebra. For those who wish to pursue the subject further *Algebra* (Teach Yourself Books), will be found most suitable.

CHAPTER 16

Ratio—Proportion—Unitary Method

Ratio

Numbers may be related to one another in various ways. That relation in which we think of the number of times the one number is contained in the other is called a *Ratio*. All fractions may be looked upon as ratios, and the placing of the numerator over the denominator as implying division. Thus, $\frac{1}{2} = 1 \div 2$, where 2 is contained in 1 half a time; $\frac{6}{3} = 2$, where 3 is contained in 6 twice, and so on. The idea of a ratio is the basis of all proportion and the student must thoroughly understand it.

First, then, we can speak of the ratio between 12 and 3, but we cannot speak of the ratio between 12 sheep and 3 cows. The quantities compared must be *of the same kind* if the ratio is to have any meaning; for it is absurd to say that 3 cows are contained in 12 sheep 4 times. But, supposing we know the value of the 12 sheep to be £90, and the value of the 3 cows to be £75, then $\frac{90}{75}$ or $\frac{6}{5}$ has a definite meaning, viz. that the *value* of the three cows is contained in the value of the 12 sheep $\frac{6}{5}$ or $1\frac{1}{5}$ times. Or, to put it in another way, the value of the 12 sheep is $\frac{6}{5}$ or $1\frac{1}{5}$ times the value of the 3 cows; and this leads us to perhaps the simplest definition of *Ratio* as *the number* (whole or fractional) *of times that one quantity is contained in another quantity of the same kind*.

Example 1. The ratio between 2p and 30p

$$= \frac{2p}{30p} = \frac{1}{15}.$$

Example 2. The ratio between 30 cm and 10 m

$$= \frac{30 \text{ cm}}{1000 \text{ cm}} = \frac{3}{100} = 0.03.$$

Example 3. The ratio of the number of hours in March to the number of weeks in April

$$= \frac{31 \times 24}{30 \div 7}$$
$$= \frac{31 \times 24 \times 7}{30}$$
$$= \frac{31 \times 8 \times 7}{10}$$
$$= 173.6.$$

Example 4. The ratio of 4 weeks 10 hours 4 minutes to 28 minutes

$$= \frac{4 \text{ weeks } 10 \text{ h } 4 \text{ min}}{28 \text{ min}}$$
$$= \frac{40 \, 924 \text{ min}}{28 \text{ min}}$$
$$= \frac{10 \, 231}{7} = 1461.7.$$

It will be readily seen that this finding of the ratio between two quantities is just the same thing as reducing the one quantity to the fraction of the other, or finding what fraction the one quantity is of the other.

EXERCISE 29

Find the ratios of:
1. 1 m³ to 1 mm³.
2. £10·05 to £25·05.
3. 1 year to 1 leap year.
4. 73 days to 1 year.
5. Log_{10} 1000 to $\log_{10}$ 100.
6. 4^2 to 7^2.

7. 4^2 to 8^2.

8. $5·85 to £2·05 (£1 = $2·50).

9. A kilo of feathers to a kilo of lead.

Which is the larger of the following ratios:

10. $\dfrac{2 \text{ kg}}{5 \text{ t}}$ or $\dfrac{2 \text{ g}}{5 \text{ g}}$.

11. $\dfrac{£7·70}{£8·30}$ or $\dfrac{£5·50}{£6·95}$.

12. $\dfrac{6\frac{1}{2} \text{ days}}{14 \text{ days}}$ or $\dfrac{3 \text{ weeks}}{7 \text{ weeks}}$.

13. A piece of land measuring 1 are is to be converted into a garden. Three-fourths of the area is to consist of garden, the rest of walks. What is the ratio of the walk area to that of the garden?

14. A man and a boy are paid £2 for a day's work. Of this sum the man gets £1·35. In what ratio has the sum been divided?

15. If the diameter of a hoop is $1\frac{1}{2}$ m, the circumference will be found to be nearly $4\frac{5}{7}$ m. What is the ratio of the circumference to the diameter?

16. Two trains run a distance of 400 km in $8\frac{1}{2}$ and 10 h respectively. What is the ratio of the two speeds?

Proportion

The ratio of 2 to 4 $= \dfrac{2}{4} = \dfrac{1}{2}$; and because these two ratios

$\dfrac{2}{4}$ and $\dfrac{1}{2}$ are equal we say that the numbers 2, 4, 1 and 2

are *in proportion*. In other words, (1) *proportion is the equality of ratios*, or (2) four numbers are in proportion when the ratio of the first to the second equals the ratio of

the third to the fourth. Examples: The ratios $\dfrac{12}{6}, \dfrac{4}{2}$ are

equal, each being equal to 2; and therefore the numbers 12, 6, 4 and 2 are in proportion.

Modes of expressing the above and any proportion are as follows:

(1) 12 is to 6 as 4 is to 2.

(2) $\quad$ 12 : 6 :: 4 : 2.

(3) $\qquad \dfrac{12}{6} = \dfrac{4}{2}$.

In practice, the problem connected with proportion is to find one of these four quantities (usually the fourth), having given the other three. The rule for finding this unknown quantity is known as the *Rule of Three*, or Simple Proportion; and its reason, or proof, may be understood from the following:

Let a, b, c, d represent any four quantities *in proportion* so that $\frac{a}{b} = \frac{c}{d}$. Now, we have already seen that a fraction is unaltered in value if its numerator and denominator are each multiplied or divided by the same number. Multiply then $\frac{a}{b}$ by $\frac{d}{d}$, which gives us $\frac{a \times d}{b \times d}$, and $\frac{c}{d}$ by $\frac{b}{b}$, which gives us $\frac{c \times b}{d \times b}$. The two fractions $\frac{a}{b}$, $\frac{c}{d}$ have thus become changed into the forms $\frac{a \times d}{b \times d}$, $\frac{c \times b}{d \times b}$. Now, since these two *equal* fractions have equal denominators (viz. $b \times d$), their numerators must also be equal. Hence $a \times d = c \times b$, that is, *the product of the first and last terms = the product of the second and third*, or the product of the extreme terms = the product of the mean terms.

But a, b, c, d stand for any numbers; therefore, the statement holds good for any numbers that are in proportion.

From this fact follows a *rule* for finding the fourth or any other term. For, since

$$a \times d = b \times c$$
$$d = (b \times c) \div a$$
$$= \frac{b \times c}{a}.$$

Or, put in words: the fourth term (d) = the product

of the second (b) and third (c) terms divided by the first (a).

That is, put in the ordinary way, the *Rule of Three* is: multiply the second and third terms together and divide by the first.

To find the other terms:

(1)   Since $a \times d = b \times c$,

$$a = \frac{b \times c}{d}.$$

(2)   Since $a \times d = b \times c$,

$$b = \frac{a \times d}{c}.$$

(3)   Since $a \times d = b \times c$,

$$c = \frac{a \times d}{b}.$$

Find the unknown term in the following:

Example 5. $x : 8 :: 12 : 16$,

$$\text{that is, } \frac{x}{8} = \frac{12}{16},$$

$$\therefore x \times 16 = 8 \times 12,$$

$$\therefore x = \frac{96}{16} = 6.$$

Example 6. $$\frac{7}{x} = \frac{19}{114},$$

$$\therefore 7 \times 114 = x \times 19,$$

$$\text{or } x \times 19 = 7 \times 114,$$

$$\therefore x = \frac{7 \times 114}{19}$$

$$= 42.$$

Example 7. $\dfrac{13}{52} = \dfrac{x}{56}$,

$$\therefore x \times 52 = 13 \times 56,$$

$$\therefore \quad x = \dfrac{\overset{14}{\cancel{13}} \times 56}{\underset{4}{\cancel{52}}}$$

$$= 14.$$

Example 8. $\dfrac{18}{14} = \dfrac{72}{x}$,

$$\therefore x \times 18 = 14 \times 72,$$

$$\therefore \quad x = \dfrac{14 \times \overset{4}{\cancel{72}}}{\cancel{18}}$$

$$= 56.$$

When *three* numbers are so related to one another that the first is to the second as the second is to the third, the *second* number is called a *mean proportional* between the other two. Thus the numbers 3, 9, 27 are so related that $3:9::9:27$; here, then, 9 is a *mean proportional* to 3 and 27.

Looking back to our letters *a, b, c, d*, we must represent a mean proportional thus, $\dfrac{a}{b} = \dfrac{b}{c}$.

Here $b \times b = a \times c$,
  or $b^2 = a \times c$;
$\therefore$ $b = \sqrt{a \times c}$.

(See under Square Root for further explanation.)

Hence the mean proportional between two numbers = the square root of the product of the two numbers.

Example 9. To find a mean proportional between 18 and 32.

$$\text{Here the mean proportional} = \sqrt{18 \times 32}$$
$$= \sqrt{576}$$
$$= 24.$$

Proof: $\frac{18}{24}$ or $\frac{3}{4} = \frac{24}{32}$ or $\frac{3}{4}$.

EXERCISE 30

Find a fourth proportional to the following numbers:

   1. 2, 3, 7.   2. 8, 4, 32.
   3. 9, 15, 27.   4. 18, 72, 108.
   5. $2\frac{1}{2}$, 3, $17\frac{1}{2}$.

Find the unknown term in the following:

6. $\frac{8}{16} = \frac{x}{36}$.   7. $\frac{3}{1\frac{1}{2}} = \frac{x}{16}$.

8. $\frac{2}{9} = \frac{x}{45}$.   9. $\frac{\frac{1}{4}}{\frac{1}{2}} = \frac{x}{16}$.

10. $\frac{\frac{3}{4}}{\frac{1}{4}} = \frac{x}{8}$.   11. $\frac{5}{x} = \frac{6}{8}$.

12. $\frac{1}{x} = \frac{8}{13}$.   13. $\frac{\frac{1}{2}}{x} = \frac{3}{9}$.

14. $\frac{7}{x} = \frac{56}{72}$.   15. $\frac{\frac{1}{4}}{x} = \frac{\frac{1}{2}}{8}$.

16. $\frac{2}{8} = \frac{8}{x}$.   17. $\frac{9}{7} = \frac{7}{x}$.

18. $\frac{3}{21} = \frac{21}{x}$.   19. $\frac{\frac{1}{2}}{\frac{1}{4}} = \frac{\frac{1}{4}}{x}$.

20. $\frac{\frac{1}{3}}{9} = \frac{9}{x}$.

Find a mean proportional to the following:

  21. 2 and 18.   22. 3 and 27.
  23. 4 and 16.   24. 5 and 45.
  25. $\frac{1}{4}$ and $\frac{1}{9}$.   26. $\frac{1}{2}$ and $\frac{1}{8}$.
  27. 3 and 48.   28. 4 and 49.
  29. 1 and 9.   30. $\frac{1}{2}$ and $\frac{1}{72}$.

Practical applications of ratio and proportion

Example 10. If it takes 12 men to do a piece of work in 5 days, how many men must be put to do a similar piece of work in 2 days?

Here there are 3 terms given, viz. 5 days, 2 days, 12 men; and the question is how to arrange these *so as to state the right proportion among them and the unknown term*. In the first place, one of the ratios must be either 5 days:2 days, or 2 days:5 days; and the other ratio must be either 12 men:required number of men, or required number of men:12 men. If we take the proportion $\frac{5}{2} = \frac{12}{x}$, we see that since the second term 2 is smaller than the first term 5, *so* the fourth term x must be smaller than the third term 12. But, on the supposition that the working power of the men is all the same, it cannot be that a smaller number of men will do the work of a larger in less time. Hence in stating the proportion we have always to consider whether the unknown fourth term is to be greater or less than the third term. If it is to be greater, then the second term must be greater than the first; if it is to be less, then the second term must be less than the first. In the example, then, a *greater* number of men are wanted to do the work in 2 days; therefore the proportion will be

less:greater: :less:greater,

that is, $\dfrac{2}{5} = \dfrac{12}{x}$;

therefore, required number of men $= \dfrac{5 \times \overset{6}{12}}{2}$

$= 30.$

Example 11. If 35 kg of sand are sold for £1127·40, what is the price per gramme?

Here the required fourth term is money, corresponding to £1127·40; as the price varies in *direct* proportion to the amount, the fourth term will be less than the third. Hence the proportion will be:

$$35 \text{ kg} : 1 \text{ g} :: £1127 \cdot 40 : \text{price per gramme},$$

i.e. price per gramme $= \dfrac{£1127 \cdot 40 \times 1 \text{ g}}{35 \text{ kg}}.$

(1) Notice that the £1127·40 is really to be multiplied by the fraction $\dfrac{1 \text{ g}}{35 \text{ kg}}$.

(2) Keep the quantities in fraction form and in their highest denominations as much as possible. This helps to keep the numbers you have to deal with small.

(3) In the present case the answer is obviously going to be in pence, but the fraction as it stands is in £g kg^{-1}. Convert this to pence by proceeding thus:

$$\begin{aligned} \text{price per gramme} &= \frac{£1127 \cdot 40 \times 1 \text{ g}}{35 \text{ kg}} \\ &= \frac{1127 \cdot 40 \times 100 \times 1 \text{p g}}{35 \text{ kg} \times 1000 \text{ g kg}^{-1}} \\ &= \frac{112\,740}{35\,000} \text{ p} \\ &= \frac{112 \cdot 74}{35} \text{ p} \\ &= 3 \cdot 22 \text{ pence (by long division).} \end{aligned}$$

Note: The above method is the shortest that can be adopted *under the Rule of Three,* and the example is worked under that rule simply *as an example of the rule.* The problem might have been solved by simply dividing the total amount of money equally among the total number of grammes, and without any reference to proportion, as follows:

$$35 \text{ kg} = 35\,000 \text{ g}$$
$$\pounds 1127 \cdot 40 = 112\,740\text{p}$$

$$\therefore \text{ price per gramme} = \frac{112\,740}{35\,000}\text{pence, as before.}$$

Example 12. If £1 is worth 119·12 Belgian francs, what is the value, in pence, of a 100-franc note?

Here the fourth term, £x, is English money and is clearly less than the third term, £1.

Hence
$$\frac{119\cdot12 \text{ fr}}{100\cdot00 \text{ fr}} = \frac{\pounds 1}{\pounds x}$$

$$\therefore \text{ value of the note, } \pounds x = \pounds\frac{100}{119\cdot12}$$
$$= \frac{100 \times 100}{119\cdot12}\text{p}$$
$$= 84\text{p (approximately).}$$

EXERCISE 31

1. The weight of 160 m of wire rope is 13·25 kgf. What is the weight of 11 m?

2. If 25 men earn £121·25 in a given time, how much will 17 men earn in the same time?

3. A housekeeper always spends the same proportion of her allowance on food. In one year she spends £56·25 on food out of her allowance of £90. The next year she spends £52·50 on food; what is her allowance then?

4. If 1 m of cloth is worth 35p, what is it worth in $? (Take $1 as £2·50.)

5. 1 m³ of lead has mass 3020 kg. Find the volume of 6 t of lead.

6. The lengths of the shadows cast by two objects at the same time are proportional to their heights. If the shadow of a man 180 cm high is 108 cm and a telegraph pole casts a shadow 7·8 m long, how high is the pole?

7. A faulty balance makes 100 g appear to weigh 101·4 gf. What is the mass when the balance reads 74 gf?

8. A debtor's assets are £609·50 and his liabilities £2714·25. How much can he pay in the pound?

9. A certain salary is £525 a year. What amount should be received between March 1st and June 11th inclusive?

10. A man can do a piece of work in 99 days, working 8 hours a day. How many days would 3 men take, working 7 hours 20 minutes a day?

The unitary method

All questions involving the idea of proportion can be solved by what is called the *Unitary Method*. The following examples will explain:

Example 13. If 6 kilo of sweets cost £2·16, what will be the cost of 8 kilo?

$$\text{Cost of 6 kilo} = £2\cdot16$$
$$\therefore \quad \text{,,} \quad \text{1 kilo} = \tfrac{1}{6} \text{ of } £2\cdot16$$
$$\therefore \quad \text{,,} \quad \text{8 kilo} = 8 \times \tfrac{1}{6} \text{ of } £2\cdot16$$
$$= £2\cdot88.$$

The reasoning is as follows: if 6 kilo cost £2·16, 1 kilo will cost *one-sixth* of the cost of 6 kilo; and if 1 kilo cost so much, then 8 kilo will cost 8 times as much. The method gets its name from the fact that from the *unit* of a given quantity we find some other unknown quantity. Thus, in the above example, from the unit price of 1 kilo we find the price of 6 kilo.

Example 14. How much does it cost to hire a motor-boat for 20 minutes if the hiring rate is per minute and the cost for $1\frac{1}{2}$ hours is £1·35?

$$\begin{aligned}
\text{Cost for } 1\tfrac{1}{2}\text{ h} &= \text{£1·35} \\
\text{,,} \qquad 90 \text{ min} &= \text{£1·35} \\
\text{,,} \qquad 1 \text{ min} &= \tfrac{1}{90} \times \text{£1·35} \\
\text{,,} \qquad 20 \text{ min} &= 20 \times \tfrac{1}{90} \times \text{£1·35} \\
&= 30\text{p.}
\end{aligned}$$

Example 15. If a baker can make 50 loaves weighing 3 kg each from a sack of flour, how many 4 kg loaves can he make from the sack?

By making 3 kg loaves,
        he can make out of the sack 50 loaves;
∴ by making 1 kg loaves,
        he can make out of the sack 3 × 50;
∴ by making 4 kg loaves,
        he can make out of the sack $\frac{1}{4} \times 3 \times 50$
$$= \tfrac{150}{4}$$
$$= 37\tfrac{1}{2} \text{ loaves.}$$

Note: In arranging the statements of any problem in proportion, the quantities that are of the same kind as the answer must come *last*.

If you consider the last fraction brought out by the Unitary Method, it will be found to be exactly the same as that which is produced by the Rule of Three. Which method, then, is to be adopted? Rule of Three, Unitary Method or a method depending on first principles alone? The reader must decide the point for himself. He will find, however, that the Unitary Method, though a little longer than the Rule of Three, is more likely to produce the right answer without waste of time. If, therefore, he experiences much trouble in dealing with this type of problem, he would do well always to use the Unitary Method.

EXERCISE 32

1. If 60 kg of apples cost £4·75, what will 350 kg cost?
2. If the half-yearly rate on a rental of £50 is £15·5, what should it be on a rental of £24?
3. A bankrupt's assets are £750 and his liabilities £2000; what will a creditor who is owed £32 actually receive?
4. If it requires 50½ m of carpet ¾ m wide to cover a room, how many metres of carpet ⅝ m wide will be necessary to cover the same room?
5. If a garrison of 5000 men has provisions for 50 days, how long can it last out if it is increased by 100 men?
6. A wages bill at £0·37 an hour is £46·62; what would it be if half the work hours were paid at 41p instead of 37p?
7. In a 2 km race between A and B, A wins by 100 m; what handicap can A afford to give B in a race of 1¾ km.
8. If the cost-of-living index number is 117 one year and 122 the next year, find how much more a housekeeper needs in the second year if she spent £73·55 in the first. (Assume that the index numbers represent her expenses accurately.)
9. A unit of electricity costs ½p. How much will it cost: (1) to run a 750-watt cooker for 2½ h; (2) to leave a 60-watt lamp on for 24 h? (A unit is a 1000 watt-hour, i.e. the amount of electricity consumed by 1 watt for 1000 h, or by 1000 watts for 1 h.)
10. A smoker consumed 56p worth of tobacco a week. How much will it cost him if he smokes at the same rate during the months of May, June and July?

The Unitary Method as applied to the solution of problems involving the idea of a complex proportion

Example 16. If 4 men working 9 h a day can do a piece of work in 3 days, how many men will be required to do the work in 2 days working 10 h a day?

Proceed by thinking only of one pair of similar terms at a time and finding the effect without regard to any of the other terms. Thus:

To do the work in 3 days at 9 h per day 4 men are required.

,,	,,	1 day at 9	,,	3×4	,,
,,	,,	1 day at 1	,,	$9 \times 3 \times 4$	,,
,,	,,	2 days at 1	,,	$\dfrac{9 \times 3 \times 4}{2}$	,,
,,	,,	2 days at 10	,,	$\dfrac{9 \times 3 \times \overset{2}{\cancel{4}}}{\underset{5}{\cancel{10} \times \cancel{2}}}$	,,

$$= \frac{27}{5}$$
$$= 5\tfrac{2}{5} \therefore 6 \text{ men are required.}$$

With a little practice you can shorten this working very considerably by thinking out the effect of two or more of the terms all in the same statement. Thus, we at once reduce the 3 days to the unit 1 and the 9 h to the unit 1, and think of the effect as multiplying in the one case by 3 and in the other by 9, which gives the expression $9 \times 3 \times 4$ by one statement instead of by two. In the shortened form the above process would stand thus:

In 3 days of 9 h 4 men are required.

$\therefore$,, 1 day of 1 ,, $3 \times 9 \times 4$

$\therefore$,, 2 days of 10 ,, $\dfrac{3 \times 9 \times 4}{2 \times 10}$ etc.

Example 17. The cost of insuring property worth £2000 for two years is £22; how much would it cost to insure property worth £2880 for three years and three months?

Insuring £2000 of property for 2 years is £22.
Insuring £1000 of property for 2 years is £11.
Insuring £1000 of property for 1 year is £5·50.
Insuring £2880 of property for 1 year is £5·50 × 2·88.
Insuring £2880 of property for 3·25 years is £5·50 × 2·88 × 3·25 = £51·48.

Example 18. A garrison of 1200 men has provisions for 10 weeks, allowing 900 g per man per day. If it is re-inforced by 350 men, what must be the daily allowance per man in order that the provisions may last 12 weeks?

1200 men can hold out for 10 weeks and receive an allowance of 900 g per man per day;

∴ 1 man can hold out for 1 week and receive an allowance of (1200 × 10 × 900) g;

∴ 1550 men can hold out for 12 weeks and receive an

$$\text{allowance of } \frac{\overset{300}{\cancel{1200}} \times \cancel{10} \times \overset{300}{\cancel{900}}}{\underset{155}{\cancel{1550}} \times \underset{4}{\cancel{12}}} \text{ g per man per day}$$

$$= \frac{90\ 000}{155} g$$

$$= \frac{18\ 000}{31} g$$

$$= 580 \cdot 6 \text{ g.}$$

Exercise 33

1. If a man earns £7 in 9 days of 6 h each, in how many days of 8 hours can he earn £8?

2. If a 240 g loaf costs 11p when wheat is £20·90 a tonne, how much will a 190 g loaf cost when wheat is £20·40 a tonne?

3. If 16½ t of provisions serve 2500 men for a fortnight, how much will be required for 3000 men for 4 weeks?

4. The cost of insuring property worth £500 for two years is 145p. How much would it cost to insure property worth £700 for 1¼ years?

5. If it costs £9·60 to carry 15¾ t of coal 36 km, how much will it cost to carry 6 t of coal 126 km?

6. A lawn-mower 32 cm wide and moving at 3 km/h cuts a certain lawn in 40 minutes. How long will it take a motor-mower 48 cm wide and travelling at 4 km/h to cut a lawn 2¼ times as big?

7. A railway embankment 2·5 km long must be constructed in 30 days, and 400 men are set to work on it. If at the end of

16 days it is found that only 1050 m are finished, how many more men must be put on to finish the work in the stipulated time?

8. A 9-kW engine pumps 16 tanks of oil through a height of 85 m in 1 h 50 min. How long will it take for a 60-kW engine to pump 3400 tanks of oil through a height of 60 m?

9. A family of three can be fed for a year for £110. How much will it cost to feed a family of seven for 5 months? It may be assumed that, owing to economies of buying on a larger scale, £0·96 in the second case goes as far as £1 in the first.

CHAPTER 17

Proportional Parts

One important practical application of the idea and method of proportion is the division of quantities into parts proportional to certain numbers.

Example 1. Water consists of 8 parts by mass of oxygen and 1 of hydrogen. What mass of oxygen is there in 35 grammes of water?

First method: In any unit of water (it may be a litre, kilogramme, etc.) there are 8 parts by mass of oxygen to 1 part of hydrogen. Hence we have to divide the given unit, 35 g, in such a way that 8 parts + 1 part shall make up the 35 g. Now the total number of parts, viz. 9, must evidently bear the same ratio to 1 (or 8) of these parts as the total number of grammes bears to the number of grammes that the 1 part (or 8) contains, that is

(1) $9:1 = 35:$ number of grammes in the 1 part;

or (2) $9:8 = 35:$,,   ,,   ,,   8 parts;

$$\therefore \text{ the 1 part of hydrogen} = \frac{35 \times 1}{9}$$

$$= 3\tfrac{8}{9} \text{ g};$$

$$\therefore \text{ the 8 parts of oxygen} = \frac{8 \times 35}{9}$$

$$= \tfrac{280}{9}$$

$$= 31\tfrac{1}{9} \text{ g}.$$

Second method: We have seen that a fraction is one way of expressing a ratio, and every problem dealing with proportional parts can be solved *more rapidly* without the statement of the proportion. Thus, in the above example, the reasoning will be as follows: There are 9 parts in all, 8 out of these 9, or $\frac{8}{9}$, are oxygen; therefore, the oxygen in 35 g is $\frac{8}{9}$ of $35 = \frac{280}{9} = 31\frac{1}{9}$ g.

This is undoubtedly the shorter and more practical way.

The truth of the result can be proved by showing that $31\frac{1}{9}$ is to $3\frac{8}{9}$ as 8 is to 1, and that $31\frac{1}{9} + 3\frac{8}{9} = 35$. Thus:

$$\frac{\frac{280}{9}}{\frac{35}{9}} = \frac{280}{9} \times \frac{9}{35} = \frac{8}{1}, \text{ or } 8:1.$$

Note: In taking the first method, a common mistake is to make the statement

$$8:1 = 35:x,$$

which is untrue; 35 is the value of 9 parts, not of 8 parts. What corresponds to 8 in the statement is $31\frac{1}{9}$, but then this is only found out through the statement

$$9:1 = 35:x.$$

Example 2. The ratio of the circumference of a circle to its diameter is $355:113$. Find the diameter of a circle whose circumference is $20\frac{2}{3}$ cm.

Here there is no need to add the parts as in the last example. We have simply:

$$\frac{\text{circumference}}{\text{diameter}} = \frac{355}{113};$$

$$\therefore \text{ diameter} = \frac{113}{355} \times 20\frac{2}{3}$$

$$= \frac{113}{355} \times \frac{62}{3}$$

$$= \frac{7006}{1065}$$

$$= 6 \cdot 578 \text{ cm.}$$

The following is typical of a great many problems connected with commerce:

Example 3. A, B and C join partnership. A contributes £3000 capital, B £4050 and C £7000. The profits of a year's trading amount to £1075. What is each partner's share?

The assumption, of course, made here is that, all other things being equal, and in the absence of any special agreement profits should be divided in proportion to the capital of each partner. In the example this proportion is

$$3000:4050:7000,$$
or
$$300: 405: 700,$$
or
$$60: 81: 140.$$

Hence A's share is 60 parts out of $(60 + 81 + 140)$; and so

$$\text{A's profits} = \tfrac{60}{281} \text{ of } £1075$$
$$\text{B's} \quad ,, \quad = \tfrac{81}{281} \text{ of } £1075$$
$$\text{C's} \quad ,, \quad = \tfrac{140}{281} \text{ of } £1075.$$

The following introduces the element of different lengths of time during which the capital is operative:

Example 4. A commences business at the beginning of the year with a capital of £2400. Three months afterwards he is joined by B with a capital of £2000. The year's profits are £275; how should they be divided between the two partners?

£2400 operating for 12 months is the same as
12×2400 or £28 800 operating for 1 *month*,

and £2000 operating for 9 months is the same as

9×2000 or £18 000 operating for 1 *month*.

Hence the process:

$$\frac{2400 \times 12}{2000 \times 9} = \frac{28\,800}{18\,000} = \frac{8}{5};$$

$$\therefore \text{A's profits} = \tfrac{8}{13} \text{ of } \pounds275$$
$$= \pounds\tfrac{2200}{13}$$
$$= \pounds169\tfrac{3}{13};$$

$$\therefore \text{B's profits} = \pounds105\tfrac{10}{13}.$$

Example 5. Divide £385 of prize money among the captain of a ship, his 2 officers and crew of 8 so that the captain shall have twice as much as each officer and each officer half as much again as each of the crew.

In such a problem it is simplest to begin with the smallest share and represent it by 1. Thus:

Let 1 = seaman's share,
$\therefore$ 1½ = officer's ,,
$\therefore$ 3 = captain's ,,

Total of seaman's shares = 1 × 8 = 8.
,, officers' ,, = 1½ × 2 = 3.
,, captain's share = 3.

$\therefore$ crew's share $= \dfrac{\overset{4}{8}}{\underset{2}{14}} \text{ of } \pounds\overset{55}{385}$

$= \pounds220.$

Officers' share $= \dfrac{3}{\underset{2}{14}} \text{ of } \pounds\overset{55}{385}$

$= \pounds\tfrac{165}{2}$
$= \pounds82\cdot50.$

Captain's share $= \pounds82\cdot50.$

Example 6. Divide £350 among 4 people in the proportion of $\frac{1}{2}$, $\frac{1}{3}$, $\frac{1}{4}$ and $\frac{1}{5}$. Turn these fractions into other forms having the same denominator; and, since the denominators are equal, the numerators will have the same ratios to one another as the original forms $\frac{1}{2}$, $\frac{1}{3}$, $\frac{1}{4}$ and $\frac{1}{5}$.

Thus: Find L.C.M. = 60,

$$\text{then } \tfrac{1}{2} = \tfrac{30}{60}, \ \tfrac{1}{3} = \tfrac{20}{60}, \ \tfrac{1}{4} = \tfrac{15}{60}, \ \tfrac{1}{5} = \tfrac{12}{60}.$$

Hence $\frac{1}{2} : \frac{1}{3} : \frac{1}{4} : \frac{1}{5} : : 30 : 20 : 15 : 12$.

Total number of parts = 77.

$$\therefore \text{1st person's share } \quad \frac{30}{77} \text{ of } £\overset{50}{350}$$
$$= £\frac{1500}{11}$$
$$= £136\tfrac{4}{11}.$$

2nd   ,,   ,, $= \frac{20}{77}$ of £350.

3rd   ,,   ,, $= \frac{15}{77}$ of £350.

4th   ,,   ,, $= \frac{12}{77}$ of £350.

EXERCISE 34

Answers should be given to the next (larger) penny; halfpennies are ignored in accounting.

1. Divide £60 among three people in the proportion of 3, 4 and 5.

2. Divide £326 among A, B and C so that A may have twice as much as B and B three times as much as C.

3. Divide a 50 m length in the ratio of 12 to 13.

4. A bankrupt's assets amount to £1375. His seven creditors claims are respectively £315, £276, £90, £75, £420, £670, £915. What part of the assets should the third creditor get?

5. £1300 is to be raised as a rate from three villages in proportion to the population. The populations in round numbers are 800, 950, 1200. What should each village contribute?

6. A starts business with a capital of £750. Six months after he is joined by B with a capital of £350; and nine months after A has started business he is joined by C with a capital of £600. The

year's profits are £475. How should they be divided among the three partners?

7. A ship's cargo, worth £4050, was insured for £3500. If half of the cargo belonged to A, ⅓ to B and the rest to C, what would each lose in the event of the vessel being lost?

8. Two graziers rent a field between them for £30·75 per year. One keeps 12 oxen in it for 7 months, and the other 15 oxen for 12 months. What should each pay? (The cost of the grazing of 12 oxen for 7 months is the same as the cost of the grazing of 84 oxen for 1 month.)

9. The main ingredients of a sort of mincemeat are 6 kg mixed fruit, 1 kg apples, 2 kg sugar, ½ kg almonds, 1 kg butter. How many kilos of each will be required for 60 kg mincemeat?

10. Divide £350·75 among 3 men, 2 women and 5 children, so that each man shall have twice as much as a woman, and each woman as much as 3 children. (If a child's share be denoted by 1, then a woman's share will be denoted by 3 and a man's share by 6.)

11. Divide £78·50 among 3 people in proportion to the fractions ⅓, ¼, ⅖.

12. Sugar is composed of 49·856 parts of oxygen, 43·265 parts of carbon and 6·879 parts of hydrogen. How many grammes of carbon are there in 1 kg of sugar?

13. The net receipts of a certain Rural District Council are £740. The services administered, and the proportions allotted to them, are as follows:

Housing	3·975 pence
Public Health and Hospitals	2·287 ,,
Ditches and Drains	4·102 ,,
Administration	6·031 ,,

Calculate the actual sums allotted to the separate services.

CHAPTER 18

Averages

The idea of an average enters very largely into commercial and other calculations. The average weight of a racing boat's crew is the weight which each man would be if the total weight of the whole crew were divided *equally* among the several units of the crew. The average run of a train during a journey is that same number of kilometres the train would have run each hour if the total number of kilometres were divided *equally* over the number of hours taken.

One object in finding an average is to form a general estimate of a quantity which takes a number of different values. Thus, if a train runs 20 km in one hour, 40 in another hour, 36 in another hour, 60 in another hour, our idea of its speed is rendered more definite when we say it runs on an average 156 ÷ 4, or 39 km an hour. Another use that an average serves is to *make comparisons easier*. Thus, if a schoolmaster wishes to compare the ages of his pupils in 1940 with the ages of his pupils in 1950 in order to find whether a younger or older class of pupils is attending school, the comparison would be almost impossible without taking the average. Again, it may be very useful in various ways to compare the consumption of a certain article per head in one country with its consumption per head in another country. This is done by finding the average. Average, in short, serves much the same purpose as percentage: both fix a *common standard* whereby we make comparisons.

The rule for finding the average is to *add the quantities and divide the sum by their number*. Wherever a 'nought' occurs among the quantities, it must be reckoned as forming part of the divisor. Thus, if in a cricket match two batsmen make 0 each, the sum total of the runs is still divided by 11, not by 9.

EXERCISE 35

1. What is the average of the following lengths: 20 km, 25 km, 30 km, 28 km, 18 km?

2. Find the average of 0·6, 1, 0·4, 8·6, 9·1, 12·3.

3. Find the average population of the following towns, whose populations (in thousands) in 1951 were: Glasgow, 1090; Birmingham 1112; Liverpool, 790; Manchester, 703; Sheffield, 513; Leeds, 505; and Edinburgh, 467.

4. A cricketer played 12 matches in the season. His runs in the 12 matches were 23, 52, 38, 0, 17, 36, 25, 40, 23, 19, 51, 79. What was his average for the season?

5. A cyclist did 50 km on Monday, 71 on Tuesday, 40 on Wednesday, rested on Thursday, 59 on Friday and 68 on Saturday. What was his average run per day?

6. What is the average of £3·63, £2·69, £4·27, £13·11, £7·42, £2·88?

7. A railway incline rises 1 m in 70 in the first km, then 1 in 100 for the next half km, then 1 in 120 for the next 1300 m. Find the average rise in the whole distance.

8. A housekeeper's average weekly outlay on fuel is 94p, on food £4·17 and on personal requirements 57p. If her weekly allowance is £6·20 and after 7 weeks she has saved £1·68, what is her average weekly expenditure on the unspecified items?

9. A sailing vessel sailed 2010 km in 8 days. What was the average rate in kilometres per hour?

10. The area of Exland is 170 km² and the average number of people per km² is 2020. Corresponding figures for Wileshire are 125 km² and 210, and for Zealand 173 km² and 350. Find the average number of people per km² in the three areas taken together.

11. The temperatures of a certain week were recorded as: 8°, 10°, 9°, 11·4°, 8°, 4°, 1°C. What was the average temperature for the week?

12. The distances covered by a train in successive hours were 61, 65, 59, 66, 67, 60, 61 km. What was the average speed for the recorded journey? (Note that the calculation may be simplified

by subtracting 59 km from all the distances, finding the average of the distances left and then adding 59 km to it.)

13. A family spends equal amounts on Christmas cards at 9p each, 10p each and 11p each. What is the average price of the cards bought? (Be careful.)

14. A car travels equal distances at 30 km/h and 50 km/h. What is its average speed?

15. The masses of a family's luggage were 42, 43, 38, 48 and 47 kg. What was the average mass?

16. 10 litres of petrol at 9·3p per litre and 6 litres at 7·2p per litre are mixed together; how much is the mixture, per litre?

CHAPTER 19

Percentages

If a person invests £375 in one business concern and gets a dividend of £10·60, and £420 in another undertaking, which yields him a dividend of £12·65, he has no means of knowing which is the more profitable investment *unless he can measure his two dividends by some common standard*. The standard found most convenient is 100. Thus by finding what his profit is on £100 of his money in each case, a man knows which is the more profitable. Again, the comparison of increases and decreases in connection with various statistics—population, trade, etc.—is more readily effected and better understood by reference to a common standard, like 100 or 1000. Thus, if the population of a small town rose from 5915 to 6512 between the years 1930 and 1940, and from 6512 to 7013 between 1940 and 1950, we can best compare the increases of the two periods by finding what was the increase on 100 in each case.

If the increase in the population was at the rate of 10 in every 100, we say that this is 10 per cent. Per cent. (Latin, *per centum*) means 'for every hundred'. 10 per cent., meaning 10 out of every 100, is the same thing as $\frac{10}{100}$ or $\frac{1}{10}$. It is usually written 10%.

In the case of a population increasing by 10%, we could express this increase by saying the population had increased by $\frac{1}{10}$. The following shows this a little more fully:

100 becomes 110, i.e. an increase of 10 on 100 $= \frac{1}{10}$.

200   ,,   220   ,,   ,, 20 ,, 200 $= \frac{1}{10}$.

300   ,,   330   ,,   ,, 30 ,, 300 $= \frac{1}{10}$.

400   ,,   440   ,,   ,, 40 ,, 400 $= \frac{1}{10}$.

etc., etc.

While problems involving 'percentage' could always be worked by Rule of Three method, the shortest and most practical method is the fractional, by which every percentage is thought of as a *certain fraction*. Thus think of

1% of a quantity as $\frac{1}{100}$ of it.

2% ,,   ,, $\frac{1}{50}$,,

3% ,,   ,, $\frac{3}{100}$,,

4% ,,   ,, $\frac{1}{25}$,,

5% ,,   ,, $\frac{1}{20}$,,

6% ,,   ,, $\frac{3}{50}$,,

EXERCISE 36

Express as fractions:

1.	60%.	2.	75%.
3.	5%.	4.	40%.
5.	$8\frac{1}{3}$%.	6.	8%.
7.	$2\frac{1}{2}$%.	8.	$2\frac{3}{4}$%.
9.	$1\frac{1}{4}$%.	10.	100%.
11.	$18\frac{3}{4}$%.	12.	$\frac{2}{5}$%.
13.	$\frac{1}{8}$%.	14.	$7\frac{1}{2}$%.
15.	150%.		

Express as percentages:

16. $\frac{1}{2}$, $\frac{1}{3}$, $\frac{1}{4}$, $\frac{1}{5}$, $\frac{1}{6}$.   17. $\frac{2}{3}$, $\frac{3}{4}$, $\frac{9}{10}$, $\frac{5}{8}$, $\frac{3}{5}$.

18. $\frac{2}{5}$, $\frac{8}{9}$, $\frac{3}{5}$, $\frac{6}{7}$, 0·5.   19. 0·75, 3, $\frac{1}{40}$, $\frac{1}{50}$, 0·375.

20. $\frac{3}{50}$, $\frac{5}{4}$, $\frac{5}{3}$, 0·25, 0·45.

The following method in dealing with percentages should be noticed:

$$5\% = \tfrac{1}{20} = 5\text{p in the } \pounds.$$
$$2\tfrac{1}{2}\% = \tfrac{1}{40} = 2\tfrac{1}{2}\text{p} \quad ,,$$
$$x\% = \frac{x}{100} = x\text{p} \quad ,,$$

Example 1. Find the value of 5% of £1764·76.

$$5\% \text{ of } £1764 = 5 \times 1764p = 8820p = £88·20$$
$$5\% \text{ of } 76p\ \ = \tfrac{5}{100} \times 76p = \tfrac{380}{100}p\ \ = £00·038$$

$$\therefore 5\% \text{ of } £1764·76 \qquad\qquad = £88·238$$

$$= £88·24$$
(approx.).

Example 2. Find the value of 2½% of £875·62½.

$$2\tfrac{1}{2}\% \text{ of } £875 = 2\tfrac{1}{2} \times 875p \quad = 2187\tfrac{1}{2}p = £21·875$$
$$2\tfrac{1}{2}\% \text{ of } 50p = 2\tfrac{1}{2} \times \tfrac{1}{2}p \quad = 1·25p \quad = £00·012\ 5$$
$$2\tfrac{1}{2}\% \text{ of } 12\tfrac{1}{2}p = \tfrac{5}{2} \times \tfrac{25}{2} \times \tfrac{1}{100}p = \tfrac{5}{40}p \quad = £00·001\ 25$$

$$\therefore 2\tfrac{1}{2}\% \text{ of } £875·62\tfrac{1}{2} \qquad\qquad = £21·888\ 75$$

$$= £21·89$$
(approx.).

EXERCISE 37

1. Find the value of 5% of: £72; £84·50; £70·87½; £63; £1975·40; 1800 m; 202 kg; 140 cm²; 30 h; 1600 m.

2. Find the value of 2½% of: £600; £300; £975; £61·85; £80·75; 350 m; 45 g; 1200 sheep; 875 ares; 10.

3. Find the value of 10% of: £16·80; £19·73; £17·67; £2·75; £369·43.

4. Find the value of 3⅓% of: £18; £3005; £6·25; £0·50; £81·45.

5. Find the value of 33⅓% of: £45; £94·50; 275·67; £172·11; £16·65.

Example 3. What percentage of 60 is 2?

$$2 \text{ is } \tfrac{2}{60} \text{ or } \tfrac{1}{30} \text{ of } 60, \text{ and}$$
$$\tfrac{1}{30} \text{ of } 100 = 3\tfrac{1}{3}:$$
$$\therefore 2 \text{ is } 3\tfrac{1}{3}\% \text{ of } 60.$$

EXERCISE 38

What per cent. is:
1. £3 of £12.
2. £5 of £45.
3. 5p of £1.
4. 5p of £4.
5. £25 of £125.
6. 3 of 6.
7. 2 of 50.
8. $\frac{3}{4}$ of 1.
9. 15p of £1.
10. 10p of £1·50.
11. 3 m of 60 m.
12. 1 day of 2 weeks.
13. £5 of £40.
14. 1 of 2$\frac{1}{2}$.
15. 7 of 63.
16. 1 of 0·5.

Worked examples

Worked examples of some of the most typical applications of 'percentages'.

1. The population of a town increases in 2 years from 130 050 to 132 651; what is the rate per cent. of this increase?

$$\text{Actual increase} = 132\,651 - 130\,050$$
$$= 2601 \text{ on } 130\,050;$$
$$\therefore \text{increase per cent.} = \frac{2601}{130\,050} \text{ of } 100$$
$$= \frac{2601}{1300·5}$$
$$= 2.$$

2. 65 g of alloy are made into coins worth £2·80. If the alloy is worth 4p per gramme, find the profit per cent.

$$\text{Value of 65 g of alloy} = 65 \times 4p$$
$$= £2·60$$
$$\therefore \text{gain} = 20p \text{ on } £2·60$$
$$\therefore \text{gain \%} = \frac{20p}{£2·60} \times 100$$
$$= \frac{20}{260} \times 100$$
$$= \frac{100}{13}$$
$$\therefore \text{gain} = 7\frac{9}{13}\%.$$

3. The gross receipts of a company are £485 000; of these 40% is taken for working expenses and 55% as a dividend of $3\frac{1}{2}\%$ on the capital of the company. How much is paid for working expenses and how much to the shareholders, and what is the capital?

$$\text{Working expenses} = 40\% \text{ of } £485\,000$$
$$= \tfrac{4}{10} \times 485\,000$$
$$= £194\,000.$$
$$Total\ dividend = \tfrac{55}{100} \text{ of } 485\,000$$
$$= 55 \times 4850$$
$$= £266\,750.$$

Of this dividend every $£3\frac{1}{2}$ represents £100 capital;

$$\therefore capital = \frac{266\,750}{3\frac{1}{2}} \times £100$$
$$= \frac{£26\,675\,000 \times 2}{7}$$
$$= \frac{£53\,350\,000}{7}$$
$$= £7\,621\,428 \text{ (approx.)}.$$

4. At what rate per cent. is the tax deduction made when $99\frac{1}{2}$p is taken from £39·75?

$$\text{Rate per cent.} = \frac{99\frac{1}{2}\text{p}}{£39\cdot75} \text{ of } 100$$
$$= \tfrac{199}{2} \times \tfrac{1}{3975} \times 100$$
$$= 2\tfrac{1}{2} \text{ (approx.)}.$$

5. A manufacturer combines 3 l of a mixture, which contains 15% of water, with 2 l of one containing 10% of water, and adds 1 l of water. Find the percentage of water in the resulting mixture.

Water in first mixture $\qquad = \frac{15}{100}$ of 3 l

$\qquad\qquad\qquad\qquad\qquad = \frac{9}{20}$ l.

Water in second mixture $\qquad = \frac{1}{10}$ of 2 l

$\qquad\qquad\qquad\qquad\qquad = \frac{1}{5}$ l.

Water added $\qquad\qquad\qquad = 1$ l.

$\therefore$ Total amount of water in the final

$\qquad$ mixture of 6 l $\qquad\qquad = (\frac{9}{20} + \frac{1}{5} + 1)$ l

$\qquad\qquad\qquad\qquad\qquad = 1\frac{13}{20}$ l.

$\therefore$ Percentage of water in final mixture $= \dfrac{1\frac{13}{20}}{6}$ of 100

$\qquad\qquad\qquad\qquad\qquad = \dfrac{\overset{11}{33} \times \overset{5}{100}}{\underset{}{20} \times \underset{2}{6}}$

$\qquad\qquad\qquad\qquad\qquad = \dfrac{55}{2}$

$\qquad\qquad\qquad\qquad\qquad = 27\frac{1}{2}.$

EXERCISE 39

1. The population of a town in 1921 was 156 014; in 1931 it had risen to 190 050. Find the approximate increase per cent.

2. In a school of 960 pupils, 500 are girls, the rest are boys. What is the percentage of boys and girls respectively?

3. Of an army of 37 000 men 1855 are in hospital. What percentage is fit for duty?

4. In a certain town of 85 016 inhabitants the deaths for a certain week were 325. What is the rate per thousand per annum?

5. A rate collector charges $2\frac{1}{2}\%$ for collecting rates. How much should he receive for collecting £1356?

6. The rateable value of a house is four-fifths of the rent, which is £52 a year. The water rate is $12\frac{1}{2}\%$ of the rateable value. What is the payment each quarter for water rate?

7. A fire-insurance premium is $\frac{3}{16}\%$ of the value of the property insured. What is the premium on £1240?

8. Gunpowder is made of 75% nitre, 15% carbon and 10% sulphur. Find the mass of each ingredient in 1·12 kg of gunpowder.

9. Three partners have capitals of £7400, £6000 and £4600 invested in a business. The first charge on the profits is 5% for depreciation of capital; after this £200 is paid to each of the

partners for management and the remainder is divided proportionately between the partners. If the profits for a certain year are £2310, what does each partner receive? (5% interest on capital means that for every £100 of capital £5 is deducted from the profits.)

10. Auriferous sand, of mass 12 kg, is known to contain 3·8% of gold. From this $\frac{11}{12}$ of the sand is removed by washing, and the part removed is found to contain only 0·6% of gold. How much gold is contained in the remaining sand?

11. There are 156 boys in the junior and 162 in the senior department of a school. If the boys constitute 65% of the scholars in the junior department and 45% of those in the senior department, what percentage are they of the whole school?

12. A man has a garden of 0·85 km². An orchard occupies 1% of the total area, a further 600 m² is taken up with the tennis court and 1% of the remainder is occupied by a rockery. What percentage of the whole remains?

13. A certain factory uses 5·5 t of coal per day. Because of modernisation, this can be reduced to 4·5 t per day. What is the saving?

14. A commercial traveller receives, as commission, 2½% on all his business above £1000. In one period he received orders of value £6101·25. What commission did he receive?

15. A family's expenditure in a particular period was as follows: food, £72·42; furnishing etc., £48·96; rent etc., £88·17; amusements, £19·73. The total expenditure was £360. Express each item as a percentage of the total.

16. A cargo is valued at £3070·50; the premium on insurance is 5%, policy duty 0·20% and commission ½%. What sum must be insured to cover the cargo and the expenses of insurance, and what is the premium?

17. What is the sum to be paid for insuring a cargo worth £2715, the premium being 1·5%, policy duty 0·15% and agent's commission ⅛%?

18. In a certain year the total number of occupied males over 12 years old in Greater London was 2 298 903, and the total number unoccupied was 369 396. Express the number of unoccupied males as a percentage of the total number.

19. In 1923 Great Britain produced 282·6 and the U.S.A. 581·5 million tonnes of coal. The U.S.A.'s percentage of the world's total production was 49·12; what was Great Britain's percentage?

CHAPTER 20

Areas of Rectangular Figures

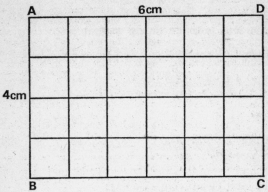

In the above diagram AD represents 6 cm and AB 4 cm. It will be seen that the rectangle ABCD contains 24 smaller areas, each 1 cm in length each way. In other words, the rectangle 6 cm long by 4 cm broad contains 24 cm².

Now, suppose we take a rectangle 4½ cm by 3¼ cm.

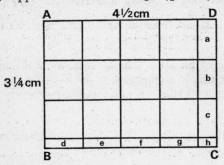

(1) The areas a, b, c are each half of the larger areas, therefore each $= \frac{1}{2}$ cm².

(2) The areas d, e, f, g are each one-fourth of the larger areas, therefore each $= \frac{1}{4}$ cm².

(3) The area $h =$ half of the area g
$= \frac{1}{2}$ of $\frac{1}{4}$, or $\frac{1}{8}$ cm².

Therefore, in the rectangle there are

$$12 \text{ cm}^2 + 3 \text{ times } \tfrac{1}{2} \text{ cm}^2 + 4 \text{ times } \tfrac{1}{4} \text{ cm}^2 + \tfrac{1}{8} \text{ cm}^2$$
$$= (12 + 1\tfrac{1}{2} + 1 + \tfrac{1}{8}) \text{ cm}^2$$
$$= 14\tfrac{5}{8} \text{ cm}^2.$$

Now, $4\frac{1}{2} \times 3\frac{1}{4} = \frac{9}{2} \times \frac{13}{4} = \frac{117}{8} = 14\frac{5}{8}$.

Hence the *area* of any *rectangular* shape is found by *multiplying the length by the breadth.*

It can be seen that the above calculation is equivalent to the multiplication of $4\frac{1}{2}$ by $3\frac{1}{4}$:

$$(4 + \tfrac{1}{2})(3 + \tfrac{1}{4}) =$$
$$(4 \times 3) + (\tfrac{1}{2} \times 3) + (4 \times \tfrac{1}{4}) + (\tfrac{1}{2} \times \tfrac{1}{4}).$$

In working problems connected with areas the following points must be clearly understood:

(1) Linear measure × linear measure = square measure.
The diagram shows this.

(2) Linear measure ÷ linear measure = a number of times, or simply a number.
Thus, 10 cm ÷ 5 cm = 2.

(3) Square measure ÷ linear measure =
linear measure.
This follows from 1.

(4) Square measure ÷ square measure = a number.

       Thus, 30 cm² ÷ 5 cm² = 6.

Or:

(1) Cm × cm = cm².

  M × m = m², etc.

(2) Cm ÷ cm = a number.

This is, of course, exactly what you would expect from what we have said in earlier chapters.

How to find the area of the walls of a room:

> Let l represent length of room,
> b ,,   breadth   ,,
> h ,,   height   ,,

Then, area of long wall $= l \times h$

∴   ,,   2 long walls $= 2lh.$

   ,,   short wall $= b \times h$

∴   ,,   2 short walls $= 2bh.$

∴   ,,   4 walls $= 2lh + 2bh$

                            $= 2h(l + b).$

Or, if the 4 walls be thought of as in one straight line, then the area of the four $= (l + b + l + b) \times h$

                        $= (2l + 2b)h$

                        $= 2(l + b)h,$

which is the same as $2h(l + b).$

The following diagram illustrates the above:

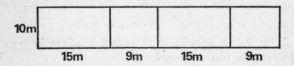

$$\text{Area} = \{(15 + 9 + 15 + 9) \times 10\} \text{ m}^2$$
$$= \{2(15 + 9) \times 10\} \text{ m}^2$$
$$= 480 \text{ m}^2.$$

The area of the sides of a cistern is calculated in the same way: the four sides corresponding to the walls of a room, and the top and bottom to the ceiling and floor.

In working problems keep in mind the following also:

(1) length × breadth = area;

hence (2) length = area ÷ breadth;

,,   (3) breadth = area ÷ length.

Example 1. Find the area of a rectangular plot of ground whose length is 20 m and breadth $12\frac{1}{2}$ m.

$$\text{Area} = 20 \text{ m} \times 12\frac{1}{2} \text{ m}$$
$$= (20 \times 12\frac{1}{2}) \text{ m}^2$$
$$= 250 \text{ m}^2.$$

Example 2. Find the cost of papering a room whose length is 5·4 m, breadth 4·2 m and height 2·4 m with paper 70 cm wide at $7\frac{1}{2}$p per metre.

$$\text{Area of walls} = 2h(l + b)$$
$$= (2 \times 2\cdot4)(5\cdot4 + 4\cdot2) \text{ m}^2$$
$$= 4\cdot8 \times 9\cdot6 \text{ m}^2.$$

Now the length of paper required, assuming there is no waste, is the area to be papered divided by the width of the paper,

$$\text{i.e. } (4\cdot8 \times 9\cdot6) \text{ m}^2 \div 70 \text{ cm}$$
$$= \frac{4\cdot8 \times 9\cdot6 \text{ m}^2}{0\cdot7 \text{ m}}$$
$$= 65\cdot83 \text{ m}.$$

∴ the cost is £(65·83 × $7\frac{1}{2}$ ÷ 100) which is £4·937 or £4·94 (to the nearest penny).

The natural waste will be amply compensated for by the unpapered windows and doors!

Example 3. The interior measurements of a rectangular box are 126 mm, 108 mm, 76 mm. Find the cost of lining the box, including the lid, with metal at $1\frac{1}{2}$p per 1000 mm².

Area to be lined is

$$
\begin{aligned}
&\text{area of 4 sides} && + \text{ area of top} && + \text{ area of base} \\
&= 2h(l + b) && + (l \times b) && + (l \times b) \\
&= (2 \times 76) \times 234 && + (126 \times 108) && + (126 \times 108) \text{ mm}^2 \\
&= 152 \times 234 && + 2 \times 13\ 608 \text{ mm}^2 \\
&= 35\ 568 && + 27\ 216 \text{ mm}^2 \\
&= 62\ 784 \text{ mm}^2
\end{aligned}
$$

∴ cost is 62 784 mm² $\times 1\frac{1}{2}$p/1000 mm²

$$
= \pounds \frac{62\ 784 \times 3}{1000 \times 2 \times 100} = \pounds 0.94 \text{ (to nearest penny).}
$$

Example 4. Find the cost of the paper required to cover a room 4·4 m long, 5·2 m wide and 3·7 m high if the paper is 80 cm wide and costs 35p per piece 4 m long, assuming that $\frac{1}{8}$ of the area is not to be covered.

$$
\begin{aligned}
\text{Area of walls} &= 2h(l + b) \\
&= 3{\cdot}7 \times 2 \times 9{\cdot}6 \text{ m}^2 \\
&= 71{\cdot}04 \text{ m}^2. \\
\text{Area to be covered} &= \tfrac{7}{8} \times 71{\cdot}04 \text{ m}^2 \\
&= 8{\cdot}88 \text{ m}^2. \\
\text{Length of paper required} &= 8{\cdot}88 \div 80 \text{ m}^2/\text{cm} \\
&= \frac{8{\cdot}88 \times 10\ 000 \text{ cm}^2}{80 \text{ cm}^2} \\
&= 1110 \text{ cm.}
\end{aligned}
$$

∴ Number of pieces 4 m long is 11·10 $\div$ 4

$$
= 2{\cdot}77 \text{ (approx.).}
$$

∴ *Whole* number of pieces needed is 3
and the cost is ∴

$$
\begin{aligned}
&3 \times 35\text{p} \\
&= \pounds 1{\cdot}05.
\end{aligned}
$$

Example 5. A room is 5 m long and 4·5 m wide. It is to be covered with a carpet so as to leave a stained border all round the room 0·7 m wide. How many metres of carpet 0·75 m wide will be required for the carpeted area, and how many square metres of stained floor will there be?

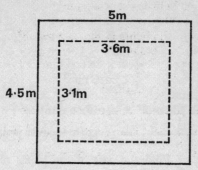

The diagram suggests a procedure for this kind of problem. The area of the stained portion is evidently the difference between the *total* area (5 × 4·5) and the inner area (3·6 × 3·1). The easiest method of finding the stained area is to work these out and then subtract the inner from the total area.

$$\begin{aligned}
\text{Total area} \quad &5 \times 4\cdot5 = 22\cdot5 \text{ m}^2. \\
\text{Inner area} \quad &3\cdot6 \times 3\cdot1 = 11\cdot16 \text{ m}^2. \\
\therefore \text{Stained area} \quad &= 11\cdot34 \text{ m}^2.
\end{aligned}$$

The carpeted area is 22·5 m².

∴ The length of carpeting required is
$$22\cdot5 \text{ m}^2 \div 0\cdot75 \text{ m} = 30 \text{ m}.$$

Example 6. How many square metres of plexiglass will be needed for a roof which will contain 200 skylights, each of 4 m × 50 cm, given that each light is to be covered by three sheets with overlaps of 10 cm and an overlap of 15 cm over the woodwork at one end?

To satisfy the conditions imposed the length of each light is

$$4 \text{ m} + 20 \text{ cm (2 overlaps)} + 15 \text{ cm}$$
$$= 4 \cdot 35 \text{ m}.$$

∴ Area of one light is $0 \cdot 5 \times 4 \cdot 35 \text{ m}^2$
$$= 2 \cdot 175 \text{ m}^2$$

and the area of 200 lights is $200 \times 2 \cdot 175 \text{ m}^2$
$$= 435 \text{ m}^2.$$

EXERCISE 40

1. Find the area of a rectangular garden plot 8 m by 5·5 m.
2. Find the area of a field 54 m × 37 m.
3. How many square metres of lino will be needed to cover a floor 350 cm long by 150 cm broad?
4. What is the area of a field whose sides are 22·6 m and 1·4 km?
5. How many metres of paper 0·25 m wide will be needed to cover a room which is 6 metres square and 4 m high?
6. How many metres of carpet 0·6 m wide will cover a room 9 m long by 8·4 m wide?
7. Find the cost of covering a floor whose dimensions are 6·25 m and 4 m with lino 75 cm wide at 17½p per metre.
8. Find the area of wall to be covered with paper in a room which is 4·3 m high, 6·4 m wide and 12·6 m long if there are 4 windows, each 1·7 m × 3·3 m.
9. In question 8, what is the area of glass in the walls, ignoring window-frames, etc.?
10. In the room in questions 8 and 9, there is a door, 1·1 m × 3·2 m. If paint costs 42p a litre and 1 litre covers 7 m² of wall, what does it cost to paint the door? (You may ignore the cost of removing the paper.)
11. Find the cost of covering the inside of an open cistern 4 m long, 3 m wide and 4 m deep with lead of mass 7 kg to the m² at £75·50 per tonne.
12. In a garden 12 m by 20 m, the central area is to be turfed and an outside path, 1 m wide all round, is to be paved. If the turf is bought in sods 2·5 metres square and paving stones in areas of 0·5 m × 3 m, and each costs £1, what is the total cost?
13. What will it cost in (a) francs, (b) sterling to carpet a floor 10 m by 8 m with carpet ¾ m wide at 50 francs per metre (13 francs to the pound)?

14. A map measures 1 m by 3·5 m and is on a scale of 1:250; what real area does it represent?

15. What area of paper is to be found in a book of 192 pages, each of which is 105 mm × 175 mm? (Be careful.)

16. If, in question 15, a band of 15 mm was trimmed from the outside edge of each page, how much paper was there before the book was bound?

17. If, on average, one tree goes to make 10 m² of paper and there are 8 trees for every 100 m² of forest, how much forest must be cut down in order to print 2000 copies of the book in question 16? You may ignore paperwork in the office, advertising, etc.

CHAPTER 21
Volumes of Rectangular Solids

The following diagram will explain the reason of the rule for finding the volume or content of any rectangular solid:

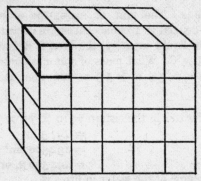

This diagram represents a solid body, 5 cm by 4 cm by 2 cm, which has been divided into cubes with 1-cm sides. The reader will see that there are 2 columns of 5 times 4 cubes, or 40 cubes in all. Hence the rule: To find volume or content of a rectangular solid multiply length, breadth and thickness together.

As in the measurement of areas, note the following in connection with volumes:

(1) Cubic measure ÷ cubic measure = a number of times.

(2) Cubic measure ÷ square measure = linear measure.

(3) Cubic measure ÷ linear measure = square measure.

Example 1. Find the volume of a block of wood measuring 178 mm long, 150 mm wide and 25 mm thick.

$$\begin{aligned}
\text{Volume} &= \text{length} \quad \times \text{breadth} \times \text{thickness} \\
&= 178 \text{ mm} \times 150 \text{ mm} \times 25 \text{ mm} \\
&= 178 \quad\quad \times 150 \quad\quad \times 25 \text{ mm}^3 \\
&= 667\,500 \text{ mm}^3 \\
&= 667{\cdot}5 \text{ cm}^3 \\
&= 0{\cdot}066\,75 \text{ m}^3.
\end{aligned}$$

Example 2. The unit of mass, the gramme, was originally defined as 1 cubic centimetre of water at 4°C. The unit of liquid capacity, the litre, is defined as 1 kg of water at 4°C. What mass of water is contained in a cistern 10 m × 5·5 m × 3·5 m and what is its liquid capacity?

$$\begin{aligned}
\text{Volume of water in the cistern} &= 10 \times 5{\cdot}5 \times 3{\cdot}5 \text{ m}^3 \\
&= 192{\cdot}5 \text{ m}^3 \\
&= 192\,500 \text{ cm}^3 \\
&= 192\,500 \text{ g, or } 192{\cdot}5 \text{ kg}
\end{aligned}$$

and the volume of the water in litres is

$$192\,500 \text{ ml, or } 192{\cdot}5 \text{ l.}$$

Example 3. A tank 10 × 7 × 5 m is filled with water which runs into it at the rate of 8 m/s through a pipe whose cross-section is 75 mm². How long will it take to fill?

$$\begin{aligned}
\text{Volume of the tank} &= 10 \times 7 \times 5 \text{ m}^3 \\
&= 350 \text{ m}^3.
\end{aligned}$$

Volume of water passing through the pipe per second is:

$$\begin{aligned}
&8 \text{ m} \times 75 \text{ mm}^2 \\
&= 800 \text{cm} \times 0{\cdot}75 \text{ cm}^2 \\
&= 600 \text{ cm}^3.
\end{aligned}$$

∴ the time for the tank to fill is

$$350 \text{ m}^3 \div 600 \text{ cm}^3/\text{s}$$
$$= \frac{350 \times 10^6 \text{ cm}^3 \text{ s}}{600 \text{ cm}^3}$$
$$= 5 \cdot 83333 \ldots \times 10^5 \text{ s}$$
$$= 583\ 333 \cdot 333 \ldots \text{ s}.$$

The answer can be divided by 60 to give the answer in minutes or by 3600 to give an answer in hours.

Example 4. A section of a stream is 2·4 m wide and 0·35 m deep. The water flows through the section at an average speed of 3·6 km/h. If 1 litre of water is 1000 cm³, how many litres of water flow through the section each day?

Area of section $= 2 \cdot 4 \times 0 \cdot 35 \text{ m}^2$
$= 0 \cdot 84 \text{ m}^2.$

Length of the column of water passing through the section daily $= 24 \times 3 \cdot 6 \text{ km}$
$= 86 \cdot 4 \text{ km}.$

∴ volume of water passing through the section daily
$= 86 \cdot 4 \times 0 \cdot 84 \text{ km} \times \text{m}^2$
$= 86 \cdot 4 \times 0 \cdot 84 \times 10^3 \text{ m}^3$
$= 72 \cdot 576 \text{ m}^3$
$= 72 \cdot 576 \times 10^6 \text{ cm}^3$
$= 72\ 576 \times 10^3 \text{ cm}^3$
$= 72\ 576 \text{ l}.$

Exercise 41

1. Find the capacity in litres of a water-tank whose length is 7 m, breadth 5·5 m and depth 6 m.
2. How much soil, in m³, can be put in a railway cutting 150 m long, 2·5 m wide and 5 m deep?
3. The weight of 1 m³ of water is 9·81 × 10³ N. What is the weight of water in a tank 10 m long, 7 m wide and 3·5 m deep?

4. Find the value of a stack of bricks, each 225 mm × 100 mm × 80 mm, which is 7·2 m × 6 m × 6 m if 3000 bricks cost £40.

5. How long is a trench which holds 50 000 l of water if it is 4 m × 3 m in cross-section?

6. A river 4 m deep and 30 m wide flows at 4 km/h. What is the rate of flow in litres per minute?

7. What volume of lead 2·5 mm thick is required to cover the sides and base of a box 2 m square and 3 m deep?

8. A plate of gold 250 mm square and 4 mm thick is hammered out so that it is 3 m². How thick is it now?

9. A block of steel 150 mm long, 100 mm broad and 90 mm deep is rolled out into a rod which has a uniform section of 108 mm². What is the length of the rod?

10. If a field of 1 a is flooded by 200 t of water, what is the average depth of water?

11. Given that, for equal volumes of ice and water, the ice has $\frac{9}{10}$ the mass of water, how many tonnes of ice can be packed in an ice store 10 × 9 × 6 m?

12. A reservoir is 8·1 m long and 4 m wide. How many tonnes of water must be drawn off so that the surface level may drop by 0·8 m?

CHAPTER 22

Areas and Volumes of Common Figures

The formulae in this chapter cannot be proved without some study of Geometry. Most of them can easily be verified by experiment, and they are given here merely for practical use; anyone who wishes to understand the theory, or to study more complex figures, would be well advised to read *Geometry* (Teach Yourself Books), where these topics are fully discussed.

Triangle

The area of the *triangle* ABC in the figure is equal to half the area of the *parallelogram* ABCD, and the latter area $= b \times h$ (square units).

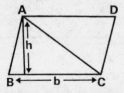

Thus area of triangle $= \frac{1}{2}bh = \frac{1}{2} \times$ base $\times$ height.

Note that any of the sides of a triangle may be considered to be the base. If one of the angles of the triangle is a *right angle* (see fig.), then the area is simply half the product of the two sides at right angles.

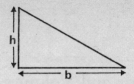

The area of any figure bounded entirely by straight lines can be found by dividing the figure into triangles and finding their areas separately.

An especially important area is that of the *trapezium*, such a figure as that shown in the diagram PQRS. It will be seen that this can be divided into two triangles,

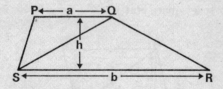

each of height h, PQS and QSR. Their areas are $\frac{1}{2}ah$ and $\frac{1}{2}bh$ respectively, so that the area of the whole figure is $\frac{1}{2}(a + b) \times h$.

Circle

The only other area we shall mention is that of the circle. The area of a circle is πr^2, where r is the radius (see diagram) and π (Greek 'pi') is the symbol always used to represent a certain number which cannot be expressed accurately as a fraction: approximate values for it are $\frac{22}{7}$, 3·14 or 3·142. A more accurate value is 3·141 59. This number is also useful in finding the *circumference* (the boundary ABDC of the circle). The length of the circumference is $2\pi r$, or πd, where d stands for *diameter* (AD in the diagram). Note carefully the difference between radius and diameter.

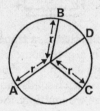

When we come to consider volumes, one simple principle enables us to apply the formulae for areas in many cases. This is that the volume of any solid which has the same *cross-section* at all points of its length is equal

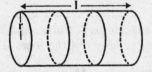

to length × area of cross-section. The cross-section of a solid is the figure obtained by making a flat (or plane) cut in any direction. Thus, a *cylinder* can be cut as shown in the diagram so that its cross-sections are all equal circles, and its volume is therefore $\pi r^2 l$, where r

is the radius of the circle of cross-section and l is its length. Or, again, a greenhouse standing against a wall has very often a constant cross-section of the shape

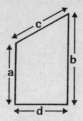

shown in the diagram, that is, a trapezium cross-section. The volume of such a greenhouse is $\frac{1}{2}(a + b) \times d \times l$, where l stands for its length, not shown in the diagram.

The surface areas of such solids can also be found by a similar method: here we multiply the perimeter (length of boundary) of the cross-section by the length of the solid. Thus the area of the curved portion of the cylinder is length $\times$ circumference of circle, or $2\pi r l$. The area of the greenhouse, front and roof, excluding ends, is $(a + c) \times l$, since $(a + c)$ is the length of the perimeter of the portion considered.

Cone

The volume of a *cone* is $\frac{1}{3}\pi r^2 h$, where r and h are the radius of the base and the height of the cone. This is perhaps

best remembered as being *one-third of the volume of a cylinder on the same base and of the same height*. The curved surface area is $\pi r l$ and, since the area of the base is πr^2, the total surface area of the cone is $\pi r l + \pi r^2$.

Sphere

The volume of a *sphere* (solid in the shape of a ball) is $\frac{4}{3}\pi r^3$, where r is its radius (not *diameter*); and its surface area is $4\pi r^2$.

The above formulae will be found sufficient to cover the areas and volumes of most ordinary figures. There is one geometrical theorem in addition which is frequently useful in finding dimensions of figures. This is called Pythagoras' Theorem (Pythagoras was an ancient Greek mathematician); it states that the sum of the areas obtained by squaring the sides a and b of a right-angled triangle (see figure) is equal to the area obtained by

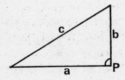

squaring c, the side opposite to the right angle. Thus, $a^2 + b^2 = c^2$. If $a = 3$ m, $b = 4$ m, for example, c can be found, for

$$c^2 = a^2 + b^2 = 3^2 + 4^2 = 9 + 16 = 25 = 5^2;$$
$$\therefore c = 5 \text{ m.}$$

Note that this theorem is true only for right-angled triangles, or triangles with a corner like that at P in the figure above. It is not true in the case of triangles like those in the figure of the trapezium on page 170.

Example 1. Find the area of glass needed for a greenhouse which is 20 m long, 2·6 m high at the front, 4 m high at the back and 4·8 m wide. The ends are of glass but contain wooden doors each 1·1 m × 2·0 m.

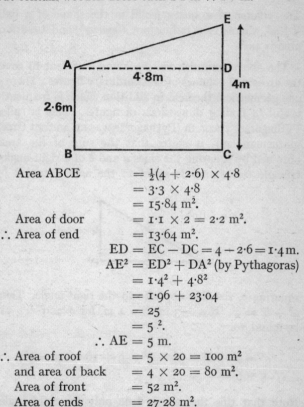

$$\text{Area ABCE} = \tfrac{1}{2}(4 + 2\cdot6) \times 4\cdot8$$
$$= 3\cdot3 \times 4\cdot8$$
$$= 15\cdot84 \text{ m}^2.$$

$$\text{Area of door} = 1\cdot1 \times 2 = 2\cdot2 \text{ m}^2.$$
$$\therefore \text{Area of end} = 13\cdot64 \text{ m}^2.$$
$$\text{ED} = \text{EC} - \text{DC} = 4 - 2\cdot6 = 1\cdot4 \text{ m}.$$
$$\text{AE}^2 = \text{ED}^2 + \text{DA}^2 \text{ (by Pythagoras)}$$
$$= 1\cdot4^2 + 4\cdot8^2$$
$$= 1\cdot96 + 23\cdot04$$
$$= 25$$
$$= 5^2.$$
$$\therefore \text{AE} = 5 \text{ m.}$$

$$\therefore \text{Area of roof} = 5 \times 20 = 100 \text{ m}^2$$
$$\text{and area of back} = 4 \times 20 = 80 \text{ m}^2.$$
$$\text{Area of front} = 52 \text{ m}^2.$$
$$\text{Area of ends} = 27\cdot28 \text{ m}^2.$$
$$\therefore \text{Total area of glass is } 259\cdot28 \text{ m}^2.$$

Example 2. Find the volume of a cylindrical box covered by a hemispherical lid if the radius of the base is 30 cm and the height from the base to the lid is 40 cm.

The box consists of a cylinder and half a sphere. The radius of both the cylinder and sphere is 30 cm and the length of the cylinder is 40 cm.

Thus the volume is $\pi r^2 h + \frac{2}{3}\pi r^3$.

$$= (\pi \times 30^2 \times 40) + (\tfrac{2}{3}\pi \times 30^3)$$
$$= 36\,000\pi + 18\,000\pi$$
$$= 54\,000 \times 3\cdot142$$
$$= 169\,668 \text{ cm}^3.$$

EXERCISE 42

1. A triangular area is cut off from the corner of a square field, the lengths of the sides at right angles being 38 m and 23 m. Find the area cut off and the decrease in the length of fencing necessary for the field.

2. A house has a gable end; the lengths of the sides of the triangle forming the gable are 5·5 m, 5·5 m and 7 m. Find the area of the gable. (Divide the triangle into two identical halves by drawing a vertical line from the apex of the gable, and find the height by Pythagoras' Theorem.)

3. A motorway goes through a cutting for 180 m where the banks are 34 m high; the cut is 26 m wide at the bottom and 42 m wide at the top. Find the volume of earth excavated in making the cutting.

4. A plot of ground has four points, A, B, C, D at its corners. B is 30 m due east of A, D is 20 m south-west of A, and C is due east of D and due south of B. Find the area of the plot and the length of fence required to enclose it.

5. A roundabout is circular and 30 m across; what is its area?

6. The frontage of a crescent of houses is in the form of a semicircle. If the direct distance from one end of the crescent to the other is 187 m, find the length of the frontage.

7. Find the volume of a spice jar 45 mm high and 23·75 mm across.

8. Find the mass of 8 m of metal piping 2 mm thick, external diameter 35 mm. 1 mm³ of the metal has mass 0·08 g.

9. Find the mass of a round bar of the metal of question 8 10 m long and 55 mm thick.

10. Find the cubic capacity of a building on a rectangular foundation 3 m by 5 m, 6 m high to the eaves, with two gable ends on the shorter sides each 1·8 m high.

11. Find the area of material needed to form the curved surface of a loudspeaker cone of radius 80 mm and depth 35 mm.

12. A rubber ball has diameter 60 mm. If the rubber is 2·5 mm thick, find the volume of the rubber. (The answer is found by subtracting the volume of the space inside the ball from the total volume of the ball: the diameter of the inner sphere is 60 mm − 2 × 2·5 mm = 55 mm.)

CHAPTER 23

Business Mathematics

Interest is money paid for the use of money. The money lent is called the *Principal*. The sum of the Principal and its Interest for any length of time is called the *Amount*. The money paid for the use of the Principal expressed as a percentage is called the *rate*, and, since this is so much per £100 per year, it is called the *rate per cent. per annum*.

There are two kinds of interest: (1) *Simple*; (2) *Compound*.

When the interest is paid yearly, or at any rate periodically, and not added to the principal, it is called *Simple*. When the interest is added to the principal and so accumulates over a period, it is called *Compound*.

Simple interest

To calculate simple interest we use the following formula:

Simple Interest

$$= \frac{\text{Principal} \times \text{Rate per cent.} \times \text{Number of years}}{100}.$$

This is written as

$$I = \frac{PRN}{100} \text{ where } \begin{cases} P = \text{Principal} \\ R = \text{Rate per cent.} \\ N = \text{Number of years.} \end{cases}$$

Example 1. Find Simple Interest on £500 for 84 days at $6\frac{1}{2}\%$ per annum.

$$\text{Simple Interest} = \frac{P \times R \times N}{100}$$

$$= \frac{84}{365} \times \frac{6\frac{1}{2}}{100} \text{ of } 100$$

$$= \frac{\overset{42}{84}}{\underset{73}{365}} \times \frac{13}{\underset{2}{200}} \times \pounds\overset{5}{500}$$

$$= \frac{\pounds546}{73}$$

$$= \pounds7 \cdot 48.$$

Example 2. Find the simple interest on £3695·75 for 1 year and 8 months at $4\frac{1}{2}\%$ per annum.

$$\text{Simple Interest} = \frac{PRN}{100}$$

$$= \pounds3695 \cdot 75 \times 4\frac{1}{2} \times 1\frac{2}{3} \div 100$$

$$= \pounds3695 \cdot 75 \times \frac{9}{2} \times \frac{\overset{3}{5}}{3} \times \frac{1}{\underset{20}{100}}$$

$$= \pounds277 \cdot 18 \text{ (approximately)}.$$

Example 3. Find the simple interest on £5006·67 for $2\frac{3}{4}$ years at $3\frac{1}{4}\%$.

$$\text{Simple Interest} = \frac{PRN}{100}$$

$$= \pounds5006 \cdot 67 \times \frac{13}{4} \times \frac{11}{4} \times \frac{1}{100}$$

$$= \pounds50 \cdot 0667 \times \frac{13 \times 11}{4 \times 4}$$

$$= \pounds12 \cdot 5167 \times \frac{13 \times 11}{4}$$

$$= \pounds3 \cdot 1292 \times 13 \times 11$$

$$= \pounds40 \cdot 6796 \times 11$$

$$= \pounds447 \cdot 475 \qquad\qquad (1)$$

$$= \pounds447 \cdot 48 \qquad\qquad (2)$$

In the above example, the principal was first divided by 100 and then by 4, and by 4 again.

The student should be careful not to discard too many places of decimals; although the answer is only required correct to two decimal places, if only two places had been kept throughout, we would have obtained £447·59 as answer—a substantial error.

Although the (1) is accurate to the nearest ½p, banks and accounting systems will not recognise any fractions of a penny in their final answers, and (2) is taken as correct.

Note: When the time during which the interest is to be calculated is from one given day to another, *one only* of these days is reckoned.

Transformation of formulae

Since Interest = (Principal × Rate per cent. × Number of years) ÷ 100; that is, $I = \dfrac{P \times R \times N}{100}$, or, what is the same thing,

$$\frac{P \times R \times N}{100} = I,$$

then it follows that

$$P = I \div \left(\frac{R \times N}{100}\right);$$

$$R = I \div \left(\frac{P \times N}{100}\right);$$

$$N = I \div \left(\frac{P \times R}{100}\right);$$

or, expressing these three facts in fractional form

$$(1) \quad P = \frac{100 \times I}{R \times N};$$

$$(2) \quad R = \frac{100 \times I}{P \times N};$$

$$(3) \quad N = \frac{100 \times I}{P \times R}.$$

Example 4. In what time will a sum of £1275 amount to £1500 at $3\frac{1}{2}\%$ simple interest?

$$N = \frac{100 \times I}{P \times R}$$

$$= \frac{100 \times (1500 - 1275)}{1275 \times 3\frac{1}{2}}$$

$$= \frac{100 \times \overset{3}{\cancel{225}} \times 2}{\underset{17}{\cancel{1275}} \times 7}$$

$$= \frac{600}{119}$$
$$= 5\frac{5}{119} \text{ years}$$
$$= 5 \text{ years } 15 \text{ days.}$$

Example 5. What principal will amount to £1600 at the end of 10 years at 5%?

Here the interest is not known, so that the formula $P = \dfrac{100 \times I}{R \times N}$ contains two unknowns, viz. P and I. But I = Amount − P;

$$\therefore P = \frac{100 \times (\text{Amount} - P)}{5 \times 10}$$

$$= \frac{100 \times 1600 - 100P}{5 \times 10}$$

$$= \frac{160\,000 - 100P}{50}$$

$$= 3200 - 2P.$$

Add 2P to both sides;

$$\therefore 3P = 3200$$
$$\therefore P = 1066\tfrac{2}{3}$$
$$= £1066 \cdot 67.$$

EXERCISE 43

1. Find the simple interest on £813·33 for 5 years 8 months at $4\frac{1}{2}$%.

2. Find the simple interest on, and amount of, £37·10 in $3\frac{1}{5}$ years at $6\frac{1}{4}$%.

3. Find the simple interest on £326 for 15 years at $4\frac{1}{2}$%.

4. Find the simple interest of £1501·25 for 1 year and 16 days at $2\frac{1}{2}$%.

5. Find the amount of £315·36 in 2 years 2 months and 2 days at $1\frac{1}{2}$%. (365 days = 12 months = 1 year.)

6. Find the simple interest on £2000 for 292 days at $3\frac{4}{5}$%. (Notice 73 days = $\frac{1}{5}$ year.)

7. Find the simple interest on £370·55 for 264 days at $2\frac{1}{2}$%.

8. Find the simple interest on, and amount of, £34 922·95 in 79 days at $2\frac{3}{4}$%.

9. Find the simple interest on £815·26 from 4 March to 4 August at $2\frac{1}{2}$% per annum.

10. Find the simple interest on, and amount of, £1890·50 from 4 April, 1970, to 3 September, 1971, at 5% per annum.

11. In what time will £8068·69 amount to £8976·41 at $2\frac{1}{2}$% per annum simple interest?

12. What sum of money will require to be invested at 4% in order to yield a person an annual income of £30?

13. At what rate per cent. simple interest will £240·30 amount to £301·58 in $5\frac{2}{3}$ years?

14. A person drew in all £1·60 of interest on a sum of money that had lain in the bank for 7 months. During this time the rate of simple interest paid was $2\frac{1}{2}$% per annum. What was the sum of money?

15. The simple interest on £300 from 2 June to 20 September is £2·26; at what rate is it calculated?

16. If a $\frac{1}{2}$p is the simple interest on 40p for a calendar month, what is the rate per cent. per annum?

17. When a rate of interest is increased from 4% to $4\frac{1}{4}$% the interest per annum is increased by £1·89. What is the principal?

Compound interest

First, if we want to know the interest for each year in £p as well as the total interest.

Example 6. Find the Compound Interest on £5050 for 3 years at 4% per annum.

$$£5\ 050$$
$$4$$
$$100)20\ 200$$

Interest for first year   =   £2 02
$$£5\ 050$$

Amount for first year   = $$£5\ 252$$
$$4$$
$$100)21\ 008$$

Interest for second year =   £210·08
$$5\ 252$$

Amount for second year = $$£5\ 462·08$$
$$4$$

=   100)21 848·32
Interest for third year   =   £218·48
∴ total interest   =   £630·56.

Second (the more common form of the problem), if we want to know the *total* interest.

Example 7.

	£5050
(1)	202·00
	5252
(2)	210·08
	5462·08
(3)	218·4832
	5680·5632
(4)	£630·5632

The interest after 3 years is therefore £630·56, to the nearest p.

(1), (2) and (3) are the results of multiplying by 4 and dividing by 100; that is, we multiply by 4 and at the same time place each digit of the product two places to the right. (4)—the total interest—is got by subtracting first principal of £5050 from the last amount £5680·5632.

Sometimes the interest is supposed to be due half-yearly or quarterly. In the former case, 2 years will be reckoned as four periods; and the interest calculated on each period will, of course, be at *half* the given rate.

Example 8. Find the compound interest on £250 for 1½ years at 2%, payable half-yearly. (Here there are 3 periods.)

		250
(1) First half-year's interest		2·5
		252·5
(2) Second half-year's interest		2·525
		255·025
(3) Third half-year's interest		2·550 25
(4)		257·575 25

∴ com. int. = (4) − 250 =   £7·575 25

i.e. compound interest = £7·58, to the nearest p.

When the rate is fractional it is better to use the following method:

Example 9. Find the compound interest on £3250·52½ for 2½ years at 2¼% per annum.

$$2\tfrac{1}{4}\% = \begin{cases} 2\% = \frac{2}{100} \\ \tfrac{1}{4}\% = \tfrac{1}{8} \text{ of } 2\% \end{cases}$$

```
                              12)6.
                              20)10·5
                              £3250·525
                                 65·0105 0
                                  8·1263 125
```

```
                              3323·6618 125  First year's
2¼% as before =  {66·4732 36      amount.
                  {8·3091 54
```

$$\text{Half-year's rate} = 1\tfrac{1}{8}\% = \begin{cases} 1\% = \frac{1}{100} \\ \tfrac{1}{8}\% = \tfrac{1}{8} \text{ of } 1\% \end{cases}$$

```
                              3398·4442 02  Second year's
                                33·9844 42      amount.
                                 4·2480 55
```

```
                              3436·6766 99  Half-year's
                              3250·525         amount.
```

∴ compound interest = £186·1516
∴ compound interest = £186·15   (approx.).

Example 10. A man saves £40 per year and invests it at the end of the year at 4% compound interest; find the amount of his savings, correct to the nearest penny, at the end of the fourth year.

```
                  £40        Amount at end of first year.
4% = 4/100 =      6·60
                 ─────
                 41·6
                 40
                 ─────
                 81·6        Amount at end of second year.
4% = 4/100 =     3·264
                 84·864
                 40
                 ──────
                 124·864     Amount at end of third year.
4% = 4/100 =     4·995 56
                 ─────────
                 129·858 56
                 40
                 ──────────
                 169·858 5   Amount at end of fourth year.
```
∴ amount = £169·86.

The calculation by the methods given above of compound interest for longer periods than three or four years becomes very laborious. In such cases it is usual to use the formula

$$A_n = P\left(1 + \frac{r}{100}\right)^n$$

where
n = Number of years
A_n = Amount after n years
P = Principal
r = Rate.

The calculations involved become quite simple when the formula is used in conjunction with log tables.

EXERCISE 44

1. Find the compound interest on £500 for 2 years at 2% per annum.

2. Find the compound interest on £625·52½ for 2½ years at 3% per annum.

3. Find the compound interest on £420 for 2½ years at 4% per annum, the interest being payable half-yearly.

4. Find what £30 will amount to in 3½ years at 4% per annum compound interest.

5. Find the compound interest on £3600, accumulated during 3½ years at 2½% per annum.

6. A man invests in a business £400, and allows it to accumulate for 2 years at 2¾%. What amount is due him at the end of the 2 years?

7. Find to the nearest penny the compound interest on £2743·87½ for 3 years at 3½%.

8. Find, without unnecessary calculation, the amount to the nearest penny at the end of 2 years of £1248 invested at 4% per annum compound interest, payable half-yearly.

9. A person borrows £200, and at the end of each year pays £50 to reduce the principal and pay interest at 5%. How much will he remain in debt at the end of 2 years?

10. Find the compound interest on £3600 accumulated during 3½ years at 2½% per annum. If for the last half-year the interest be reduced to 1⅞% per annum, what will be the difference in the whole amount?

(For the following use the compound interest formula.)

11. Find the amount of £250 after 10 years at $3\frac{1}{2}\%$ compound interest.

12. Find the compound interest on £133·75 for 25 years at $4\frac{1}{2}\%$.

13. Find the compound interest on £2716 for 5 years at $2\frac{1}{2}\%$.

14. Find the amount of £364 at 5% compound interest after (*a*) 13 years, (*b*) 19 years.

Profit and loss

An application of percentages (see Chapter 19) is in problems on Profit and Loss. There is little new to be learned; the principle at the bottom of the solution of every problem is the same as you have met before.

Before working an example of each case likely to be met with in actual practice, we would draw attention to the following points:

(1) A profit or loss per cent. means that the percentage is calculated *on the cost price*. Thus, suppose there is a profit of 10% on the sale of an article, the selling price $=$ $(100 + 10)\% = 110\%$ (of cost price).

If there is a loss of 10%, then selling price $=$ $(100 - 10)\% = 90\%$ (of cost price).

(2) In a complicated transaction, where an article passes through the hands of several persons before it reaches the consumer, each person (manufacturer, merchant, etc.) calculates the profit or loss as a percentage, not on the original cost price but *on his own cost price*.

Example 11. What is the profit per cent. gained by selling at £15 an article which cost £12?

Gain on £12 is £3;

that is, profit $= \frac{3}{12} = \frac{1}{4}$ of cost price.

Now, on the supposition that cost price is £100, profit per cent. must $= \frac{1}{4}$ of 100 $= 25$.

Example 12. I bought an article for £1·64 and sold it for £1·56. What was my loss per cent?

Loss on £1·64 is 8p,

$$\text{i.e. loss} = \frac{8p}{£1·64} \text{ of cost price}$$

$$= \frac{8}{164}$$

$$= \frac{1}{20·5}$$

$$\therefore \text{loss per cent} = \frac{1}{20·5} \text{ of 100}$$

$$= 4·9\%.$$

Example 13. A man buys 2·5 tonnes of scrap at $23\frac{1}{2}$p per kg. Allowing $2\frac{1}{2}\%$ for waste, at what price must he sell it per kg in order to gain not less than 25%?

$$\text{Cost of 2·5 t} = 2·5 \times 1000 \times 23\frac{1}{2}p$$

$$= £\frac{2·5 \times 1000 \times 23·5}{100}$$

$$= £587·50.$$

Selling price must be
$$£587·50 + 25\% \text{ of } £587·50$$
$$= £587·50 + £146·87\frac{1}{2}$$
$$= £734·37\frac{1}{2}.$$

$$2·5 \text{ t} - 2\frac{1}{2}\% \text{ of } 2·5 \text{ t} = \left(2·5 - \frac{2·5}{100} \times 2·5\right) \text{t}$$

$$= (2·5 - 0·062\ 5) \text{ t}$$

$$= 2·437\ 5 \text{ t.}$$

$$\therefore \text{price per t must be } \frac{£734·37\frac{1}{2}}{2·4375}$$

$$\therefore \text{price per kg must be } \frac{£734·37\frac{1}{2}}{2·4375 \times 1000}$$

$$= £0·301.$$

∴ price must be at least $30\frac{1}{2}$p if the gain is to be not less than 25%.

Example 14. One bookseller allows $\frac{1}{6}$ discount off the published price and 5% off the remaining price; another allows 20% off the published price. Which terms are better? And find the difference in costs on £100 (published price) of books.

First bookseller allows $\frac{1}{6}$ off published price

$$+ \tfrac{5}{100} \text{ of } \tfrac{5}{6} \text{ off published price}$$
$$= \tfrac{1}{6} + \tfrac{1}{24} = \tfrac{5}{24} \text{ off published price}$$
$$= \tfrac{5}{24} \times 100\%$$
$$= 20\tfrac{5}{6}\%.$$

Second bookseller allows 20%.

∴ first terms are better by $\frac{5}{6}$%, and the saving on £100-worth of books will be £$\frac{5}{6}$ = £0·83.

Example 15. A merchant mixes wines at 75p, £1 and £1·25 a litre in the proportion of 2:3:1, and sells the mixture at £1 a litre. What is his gain or loss per cent.?

$$2 \text{ l at } £0\cdot75 = £1\cdot50$$
$$3 \text{ l at } £1\cdot00 = £3\cdot00$$
$$1 \text{ l at } £1\cdot25 = £1\cdot25$$
∴ 6 l of mixture costs £5·75
6 l of mixture sells for $6 \times £1 = £6$
∴ gain per 6 litres = £$(6\cdot00 - 5\cdot75) = £0\cdot25$
∴ gain per cent. $= \dfrac{£0\cdot25}{£5\cdot75} \times 100 = \dfrac{100}{23} = 4\tfrac{8}{23}.$

EXERCISE 45

1. A man buys an article for 5p and sells it for 6p. What is his gain per cent.?

2. A merchant buys 640 items for £2·40 and the cost of packing is 6% extra, while the cost of carriage is 50p. 3% of the items are damaged. At what price must he sell the items so as to gain at least 80p on every 100 sold?

3. 48 litres of fruit juice at 28p per litre, 2·7 litres at 32p per litre and 7·6 litres at 34½p per litre are all mixed with 18 litres of water; the mixture is sold at 25p per litre. What is the gain per cent.?

4. A bookseller buys a certain class of books at 20p each. What must he charge for each book so as to make a profit of at least 18%.

5. A man buys goods at the rate of £7·50 per kg, and retails them so as to make 5% profit. (The cost of carriage is 1½p per 25 g.) 5% of the goods are stolen. Does he make a profit or a loss? And by how much?

6. An electric fire uses 1·5 kilowatts in one hour (kWh). It is used for 25 minutes every day. The cost of 1 unit (i.e. 1 kWh) is either 0·48p (power rate) or 2·6p (light rate). The cost of installing the special plug necessary to make the cheaper rate available is £1·09. What is the gain per cent. in eight years due to installing the special plug?

7. A housekeeper needs 48 eggs a month for cooking purposes. She pickles eggs in June bought at 20p a dozen for use during the months October to March. The cost of pickling is 75p. If she bought the eggs as she needed them they would cost: 24p (Oct.); 25p (Nov.); 26p (Dec.); 27½p (Jan. and Feb.) and 26p (March) per dozen. Express her profit as a percentage of what she might have spent in this period.

8. A dealer bought some stock for £292·28. He sold a quarter of it for £93·35 and the remainder for £250. Find his gain per cent. on the two portions separately and on the whole transaction.

Answers

Exercise 1, page 14

1. Ten plus ten plus ten plus ten plus ten equals five times ten equals ten times five equals one hundred divided by two equals five squared times two equals ten squared divided by two.

2. (1) 73   (2) 1600   (3) 1446
3. (1) 83   (2) 128   (3) 597
4. (1) 69   (2) 86   (3) 237
5. (1) 418   (2) 735   (3) 11 826
6. (1) 76   (2) 281   (3) 56
7. 399
8. (1) 36   (2) 49   (3) 8
9. (1) 9   (2) 8   (3) 7
10. (1) Yes   (2) Yes   (3) Yes   (4) Yes

Exercise 2, page 24

1. $2a$
2. $-17b$
3. $-6x$
4. $-6d$
5. $-12x^2$
6. $-9xy$
7. $-7x^2y$
8. $12a + 8c + d$
9. $14xy + 5b$
10. $13a^2 + 3ab$
11. (a) $-3cx - cy + yz$; (b) 3
12. (a) $ax + bx - 7cx$; (b) -126
13. $4x - \frac{23}{12}xy - \frac{1}{2}y$
14. $\frac{1}{4}a^3 - 4a^2b + b^3$
15. $12a - \frac{7}{3}c$

Exercise 3, page 27

1. $-9a - c$
2. $-12x + 3y - 3z$
3. $-9ab + xy + z$
4. $-2x^2$
5. $-8xy - 2yz + 2xz$
6. $-8p - 2q + r$
7. $2p - q + 2r - s$
8. $2ab + bc$
9. $-5pq + 4qr - 3s$
10. $-8x^2 + 6y^2 + 2z^2$
11. $\frac{3}{2}x^2 + y^2 - \frac{1}{4}z^2$
12. $\frac{7}{12}ab + \frac{5}{8}bc - \frac{1}{4}cd$

Exercise 4, page 32

1. $2a^3b^3c^4$
2. $-2x^4y^5z$
3. $x^3 + x^2y$
4. $x^4 + 2x^3y + x^2y^2$
5. $a^2 + 2ab + b^2 + ac + bc$
6. $a^3 + 3a^2b + 3ab^2 + b^3$
7. $3x^4 - x^2y^2 + 3x^2y - y^3$

8. $a^3 - a^2b - ab^2 - a^2c + b^2c + b^3$
9. $x^3 + x^2y - xy^2 - y^3$ 10. $x^3 - x^2y - xy^2 + y^3$
11. $a^4 - 2a^2b^2 + b^4$
12. $2a^2 - 3ab + 3a - 2b^2 - b + 1$ 13. $\frac{1}{8}x^4 - \frac{1}{8}y^4$
14. $\frac{1}{2}xy^3 - \frac{1}{2}xy^2z + \frac{1}{2}xyz^2 - \frac{1}{2}xz^3$ 15. $x^6 - y^6$

Exercise 5, page 35

1. $3a$ 2. $-4b$ 3. $-4xz$
4. $a + b$ 5. $a + b$ 6. $a - b$
7. $a^2 + ab + b^2$ 8. $a^2 - ab + b^2$ 9. $a - b + \dfrac{2b^2}{a-b}$
10. $a^2 - 3ax + x^2$ 11. $2x^2 + xy + 3y^2$
12. $x^4 + ax^3 - a^3x - a^4$ 13. $x^2 - a^2$
14. $x^2 - 2xy + y^2$ 15. $p^3 - 3p^2q + 3pq^2 - q^3$

Exercise 6, page 39

1. 2   2. 5   3. 2
4. 2   5. 51   6. 37

Exercise 7, page 41

1. 60   2. 1260   3. 144
4. 1260   5. 78   6. 34 944

Exercise 8, page 47

1. 44   2. 84   3. 13
4. 25   5. 32   6. 252
7. 219   8. $36 + 2 = 38$
9. $A = 30 \div 5 = 6$ 10. $P = 48 \div 16 = 3$
11. $P = 36 \div 6 = 6$ 12. $P = 84 \div 3 = 28$
13. 286 320; 626 325; 876 855; 1 288 440
14. 4 773 690; 20 049 498; 34 370 568
15. 9 427 930; 94 279 300; 942 793 000; 9 427 930 000
16. 96 499;   103 922;   111 345;   118 768;   126 191;   133 614;
141 037
17. 2 239 475; 6 718 425; 11 197 375
18. 1230, remainder 6; 1025, remainder 6; 769; 256, remainder 24
19. 5892, remainder 1; 4285, remainder 3; 3491, remainder 16; 872, remainder 97
20. 9845, remainder 6; 984, remainder 56; 98, remainder 456; 9, remainder 8456

Exercise 9, page 51

1. $a + b - c - d$
2. $2a - 2b - 3c + 3d$
3. $-a + b - c + d$
4. $-2a + 2b + c - d$
5. $2a + b + c$
6. $\frac{1}{3}x$
7. $-q + r + s$
8. $4x - 2y$
9. $4q + 2r - 2s$
10. $-2ab + 2cd + 2ef$
11. $-(p + q) - (r - s)$
12. $(2p - q) + (r - s)$
13. $-(xy + yz) - (p + 2q) + (r - s)$
14. $(6ab - 2bc) - (3cd + 4de) - (5ef - 6fg)$
15. $-(p - q) + (2r - s) - (t - w)$
16. $-2(q + 2q) - (r - s) - 2(t + w)$

Exercise 10, page 52

1. 17
2. 77
3. 300
4. -144
5. 2
6. $7\frac{1}{3}$
7. $\frac{25}{64}$
8. -6300
9. $15\,750$
10. $5835\frac{29}{32}$

Exercise 11, page 54

1. 101
2. 0
3. $\frac{1}{96}$
4. $26\frac{1}{2}$
5. 11
6. $-\frac{5}{48}$
7. $64\frac{1}{24}$
8. $1\frac{1}{24}$
9. $\frac{5}{6}$
10. $\frac{11}{12}$

Exercise 12, page 59

1. $\frac{9}{10}, \frac{1}{2}, \frac{1}{3}, \frac{13}{19}$
2. $0, \frac{7}{12}, \frac{1}{72}$
3. $£2\frac{11}{200}$
4. $4\frac{197}{240}$ t
5. $\frac{12}{35}$
6. $\frac{4}{9}, \frac{12}{13}$
7. $\frac{11}{45}$
8. $\frac{7}{80}$
9. $\frac{8}{9}, \frac{2}{3}, \frac{6}{10}, \frac{4}{7}, \frac{5}{9}$
10. $8\frac{4}{7}$ min
11. $17\frac{1}{7}$ h
12. $\frac{10}{41}, \frac{31}{41}$

Exercise 13, page 61

1. $\frac{5}{2} = 2\frac{1}{2}$
2. $\frac{3}{7}$
3. $\frac{10}{3} = 3\frac{1}{3}$
4. 2
5. $\frac{9}{4} = 2\frac{1}{4}$
6. $\frac{4}{7}$
7. $\frac{45}{7} = 6\frac{3}{7}$
8. 3
9. $£10$
10. 625 m
11. $7 \times \frac{1}{2}$ m $= \frac{7}{2} = 3\frac{1}{2}$ m
12. $\frac{18}{5}$ t $= 3\frac{3}{5}$ t
13. $\frac{1}{4}$
14. $\frac{1}{25}$
15. $\frac{2}{25}$
16. $\frac{15}{28}$
17. $\frac{7}{8}$ m
18. $\frac{10}{48}$ km or $\frac{5}{24}$ km
19. $\frac{3}{4}$ of $\frac{5}{2} = \frac{15}{8} = 1\frac{7}{8}$
20. $\frac{5}{8}$ of $\frac{15}{2} = \frac{75}{16} = 4\frac{11}{61}$ t
21. $\frac{3}{5} \times \frac{81}{10} = \frac{243}{10} = 24\frac{3}{10}$ square metres
22. $\frac{7}{8} \times 35\frac{1}{2} = \frac{7}{8} \times \frac{71}{2} = \frac{497}{16} = £31\frac{1}{16}$
23. $\frac{9}{10} \times \frac{141}{4} = \frac{1269}{40} = 31\frac{29}{40}$ litres
24. $\frac{4}{7} \times \frac{7}{2} = 2$ pence

EXERCISE 14, page 63

1. Each part $= \frac{5}{24}$ 2. $\frac{5}{42}$ 3. $\frac{4}{75}$
4. $\frac{8}{72} = \frac{1}{9}$ 5. $\frac{1}{70}$ 6. 50
7. $\frac{64}{24} = 21\frac{1}{3}$ 8. $\frac{20}{21}$ 9. $\frac{15}{56}$
10. $\frac{3}{24}$ 11. $60 \times \frac{4}{3} = 80$
12. $1260 \times \frac{2}{7} = 360 + 1 = 361$ posts
13. 68 and $\frac{2}{3}$ cm over   14. 136 times and $\frac{2}{3}$ of a time

EXERCISE 15, page 65

1. $\frac{x}{4y}, \frac{7x}{y}, \frac{x^3}{2y^3}$ 2. $\frac{ac}{b}, ce, \frac{p^2}{q}$ 3. $\frac{3p}{qr}, \frac{18mn}{l}, \frac{4s^2}{v^2}$

4. $\frac{3x + 2x}{6} = \frac{5x}{6}$ 5. $\frac{115x}{24}$ 6. $\frac{3m - 2n}{24}$

7. $\frac{pqr + 2pq}{r^2} = \frac{pq(r + 2)}{r^2}$ 8. $\frac{8x + 4x - 3x}{24} = \frac{9x}{24} = \frac{3x}{8}$

9. $\frac{37x}{60}$ 10. $\frac{-4a^2b^2}{9}$ 11. $\frac{84}{5}y^3$

12. $\frac{27q}{2p^2}$ 13. $\frac{ab^3c}{mnpq}$ 14. $-\frac{1}{ab}$

15. $\frac{9b^3x^2}{4p}$ 16. $-\frac{210a^3c}{b}$

EXERCISE 16, page 69

1. 47·480   2. 96·9059   3. 132·042
4. 9821·9415   5. 2179·442 119   6. 0·75
7. 7·837 05   8. 2·65   9. 10·991
10. 0·0045

EXERCISE 17, page 73

1. 0·407   2. 59·285   3. 720·810 09
4. 0·000 005 4   5. 7723·248 75   6. 7
7. 3·804 . . .   8. 18 200   9. 4330
10. 0·010 01   11. 1650·94 . . .   12. 1000
13. 0·000 35   14. 2·67 . . .
15. 56 866 times, and a remainder of $\frac{10}{12}$ or $\frac{2}{3}$ of 0·015 = 0·01
16. 43·75 m   17. 101·76 h
18. 135 pieces and $\frac{5}{12}$ of a piece = 0·05 cm

EXERCISE 18, page 77

1. $\frac{31}{163}$ 2. 0·0125   3. 0·0238 (approx.)
4. $7\frac{1}{2}$P   5. $7\frac{1}{2}$P   6. £0·3625

7. 0·928 571 4 (285714 repeats indefinitely)
8. (1) 0·698   (2) 0·697   9. £40·06
10. (1) 0·644   (2) 0·857   (3) 1·166
11. £20·19   12. 0·384 ¢   13. £1296
14. (1) 1019·92 newtons   (2) 2·5742 newtons

EXERCISE 19, page 81

1. 64; 144; 625; 1024   2. 2; 5; 2; 4
3. $\frac{1}{64}$; $\frac{1}{144}$; $\frac{1}{625}$; $\frac{1}{256}$ 4. 1; 1; 1; 1
5. 2; 5; 4$\sqrt{2}$; 4   6. 8; 8; 8; $\frac{1}{8}$

7. $\sqrt[b]{x^a}$; $\sqrt[a]{x^b}$; $\dfrac{1}{\sqrt[b]{x^a}}$; $\sqrt[1]{x^a}$ 8. 9; $\frac{1}{9}$; $\frac{1}{8}$; $\dfrac{1}{\sqrt[b]{x^a}}$

9. 8; $\frac{1}{8}$; 2; 2
10. $\sqrt{4} = 2$ or -2; $\sqrt{y} = x$ or $-x$

EXERCISE 20, page 84

1. 3^{11} 2. 3^7 3. $9^{11/2}$; $9^{7/2}$
4. 12^{1+2a} 5. 12^{1-a} 6. $12^{(1-a)/2}$
7. $12^{(1-a)/2+b}$ 8. $12^{\frac{1}{2}}$ 9. $10^{0·30}$
10. $10^{1·26}$ 11. $10^{0·26}$ 12. $10^{2·26}$
13. $10^{-0·74}$ 14. $10^{-1·74}$

EXERCISE 21, page 91

1. 1; 3; 4; 2; 0; 5; 1; 3; 0; 0
2. (1) 0·7782; 1·7782; 2·7782; 4·7782
   (2) 0·6721; 2·6721; 4·6721
   (3) 0·5623; 2·5623; 3·5623
   (4) 1·2467; 2·2467; 4·2467
   (5) 0·1504; 3·1659; 3·8433
3. (1) 467·7; 467 70; 46·77
   (2) 75·16; 7516; 7·516
   (3) 1·668; 166·8; 16 680
   (4) 1046; 1045; 2·004

EXERCISE 22, page 93

(These answers are corrected to the appropriate accuracy.)
1. 1139   2. 6096   3. 34 740
4. 695   5. 2·18   6. 12·2
7. 119   8. 87·7   9. 5·27
10. 446   11. 550·8   12. 2555
13. 1·08   14. 140   15. 2·013
16. 1·551   17. 2·081   18. 5·09
19. 2·38   20. 4·18

EXERCISE 23, page 98

1. (1) $\bar{1}\cdot8044$ (2) $8\cdot4010$
2. (1) $\bar{2}\cdot4498$ (2) $1\cdot1225$ (3) $0\cdot3989$ (4) $2\cdot4782$
3. (1) $\bar{2}\cdot5728$ (2) $\bar{4}\cdot6226$ (3) $\bar{1}\cdot0346$ (4) $\bar{1}\cdot6738$
   (5) $\bar{1}\cdot5438$ (6) $\bar{1}\cdot0878$
4. (1) $\bar{1}\cdot0945$ (2) $\bar{2}\cdot8291$ (3) $\bar{1}\cdot5174$ (4) $0\cdot2855$
5. (1) $\bar{1}\cdot7439$ (2) $\bar{1}\cdot7531$ (3) $\bar{2}\cdot9391$ (4) $\bar{2}\cdot2469$
   (5) $\bar{1}\cdot537$
6. $19\cdot7$ 7. 2968 8. $4\cdot93$

EXERCISE 24, page 108

1. $94\cdot096$ m   2. $924\cdot274\ 948$ km
3. $0\cdot115\ 895$ km^2; this is an area
4. 500 5. (1) 4420 m   (2) $4\cdot42$ km
6. $541\cdot86$ miles   7. $10\ 000$ 8. $0\cdot96$ fr

EXERCISE 25, page 112

1. $x = -1$ 2. $x = 4\frac{1}{3}$ 3. $x = 5$
4. $x = -5\frac{1}{2}$ 5. $p = 2\frac{1}{4}$ 6. $x = 31$
7. $x = \frac{4}{11}$ 8. $x = 6\frac{4}{7}$ 9. $x = 41\frac{2}{23}$
10. $x = -\frac{26}{33}$ 11. $x = \frac{5}{41}$ 12. $x = 7\frac{6}{19}$
13. $x = 17\frac{41}{47}$ 14. $x = -30$
15. $x = -\frac{41}{17} = -2\frac{7}{17}$ 16. A $= 66$
17. V $= 1706\frac{2}{3}$ 18. $s = 788\cdot9$
19. $s = \frac{112}{55} = 2\cdot03\ldots$ 20. $a = \frac{589}{50} = 11\cdot78$
21. $m = 9\cdot6$
22. $v^2 = 1500$, $\therefore v = \sqrt{1500} = 38\cdot7$
23. $w = \frac{3900}{11} = 354\cdot54$ 24. V $= 104$
25. $f = 5\cdot6$ 26. I $= 30$
27. P $= 857\frac{1}{7}$ 28. N $= \frac{55}{64}$
29. R $= 2\frac{74}{203}$ 30. (1) A $= 1200$; (2) $h = 11\frac{1}{4}$

EXERCISE 26, page 117

1. $72 - p$ 2. $p - q$
3. $\frac{p}{3\frac{1}{2}} = \frac{2p}{7}$ 4. $\frac{350}{x}$ h
5. $\pounds(\frac{1}{200}m + \frac{1}{2}n)$ 6. $(100x + y)$ pence
7. $\frac{b}{c}$ h   8. $\frac{k}{q}$ km per hour
9. $\frac{16z}{1000}t$ 10. $6p$ km

EXERCISE 27, page 117

1. 4 cm and 12 cm
2. £200, £800
3. 28·8 m
4. $50x + 5(74 - x) = 1135$; no. of 50p-pieces is 17, 5p-pieces is 57
5. A gets £210, B and C each get £70
6. 10 kilo
7. A gets £26, B gets £18 and C gets £16
8. In 6 h

EXERCISE 28, page 123

1. $x = 3, y = 1$
2. $y = 2, x = 2$
3. $p = 5, q = -7$
4. $y = 6, x = 5$
5. $y = -3, x = -7$
6. $B = \frac{17}{7}, A = \frac{2}{7}$
7. $B = \frac{3}{5}, A = -\frac{27}{5}$
8. $a = \frac{55}{4}, c = -10$; $\therefore F = \frac{55}{4} B - 10$
9. 23 and 17
10. 1 kg of sugar costs 8p; 1 kg of tea costs 72p
11. Boy receives $62\frac{1}{2}$p, man receives £1·$12\frac{1}{2}$
12. $a = \frac{4}{13}, b = \frac{21}{13}$
13. $a = \frac{37}{104}, b = \frac{159}{13}$

EXERCISE 29, page 126

1. $10^9 : 1$
2. $201 : 501$
3. $365 : 366$
4. $1 : 5$
5. $3 : 2$
6. $16 : 49$
7. $1 : 4$
8. $234 : 205$
9. $1 : 1$
10. 2nd
11. 1st
12. 1st
13. $1 : 3$
14. $27 : 13$
15. $22 : 7$
16. $20 : 17$

EXERCISE 30, page 131

1. $10\frac{1}{2}$
2. 16
3. 45
4. 432
5. 21
6. 18
7. 32
8. 10
9. 8
10. 24
11. $6\frac{2}{3}$
12. $1\frac{5}{8}$
13. $1\frac{1}{2}$
14. 9
15. $2\frac{4}{7}$
16. 32
17. $5\frac{4}{9}$
18. 147
19. $\frac{1}{8}$
20. 243
21. 6
22. 9
23. 8
24. 15
25. $\frac{1}{6}$
26. $\frac{1}{4}$
27. 12
28. 14
29. 3
30. $\frac{1}{12}$

EXERCISE 31, page 134

1. 0·91 kgf
2. £82·45
3. £84
4. $0·14
5. 1·99 m³
6. 13 m
7. 72·8 g
8. 22½p
9. £148
10. 36 days

EXERCISE 32, page 137

1. £27·71
2. £7·44
3. £12
4. 60·6 m
5. 49 days (49$\frac{1}{31}$)
6. £49·14
7. Any length less than 87½ m
8. £3·14
9. (1)$\frac{15}{16}$p; (2) 0·72p
10. £7·36

EXERCISE 33, page 139

1. 7$\frac{5}{7}$ days
2. 8½p
3. 39·6 t
4. £1·27
5. £12·80
6. 45 min
7. 232
8. 41 h 15 min
9. £102·67

EXERCISE 34, page 145

1. £15, £20, £25
2. £32·60, £97·80, £195·60
3. 24 m and 26 m
4. £44·82
5. £352·54; £418·64; £528·82
6. £331·39; £77·33; £66·28
7. £275; £183·33; £91·67
8. £9·78; £20·97
9. 34$\frac{2}{7}$ kg; 5$\frac{5}{7}$ kg; 11$\frac{3}{7}$ kg; 2$\frac{6}{7}$ kg; 5$\frac{5}{7}$ kg
10. Each child gets £12·10
    Each woman gets £36·29
    Each man gets £72·57
11. £19·62; £26·17; £32·71
12. 432·65 g
13. Housing: £179·42;
    Health: £103·22;
    Ditches: £185·15;
    Administration: £272·21

EXERCISE 35, page 148

1. 24½ km
2. 5·333 . . . = 5·$\dot{3}$ (3 recurring)
3. 740 (thousand)
4. 33·58 runs
5. 48 km
6. £5·67
7. About 1 in 74
8. 28p
9. 10½ km/h (approx.)
10. 384
11. 7·33°C
12. 62·71 km/h
13. 9·9p
14. 37½ km/h
15. 43·6 kg
16. 85·1p

EXERCISE 36, page 151

1. $\frac{3}{5}$ 2. $\frac{3}{4}$ 3. $\frac{1}{20}$
4. $\frac{2}{5}$ 5. $\frac{1}{12}$ 6. $\frac{2}{25}$
7. $\frac{1}{40}$ 8. $\frac{11}{400}$ 9. $\frac{1}{80}$
10. 1 11. $\frac{3}{16}$ 12. $\frac{1}{250}$
13. $\frac{1}{800}$ 14. $\frac{3}{40}$ 15. $1\frac{1}{2}$
16. $50, 33\frac{1}{3}, 25, 20, 16\frac{2}{3}$ 17. $66\frac{2}{3}, 75, 90, 62\frac{1}{2}, 60$
18. $40, 88\frac{8}{9}, 80, 87\frac{1}{2}, 50$ 19. $75, 300, 2\frac{1}{2}, 2, 37\frac{1}{2}$
20. $6, 125, 120, 25, 45$

EXERCISE 37, page 152

1. (1) £3·60   (2) £4·22½   (3) £3·54   (4) £3·15
   (5) £98·77   (6) 90 m   (7) 10·1 kg   (8) 7 cm²
   (9) 1½ h   (10) 80 m
2. (1) £15   (2) £7·50   (3) £24·37½   (4) £1·55
   (5) £2·02   (6) 8·75 m   (7) £1·12½   (8) 30 sheep
   (9) 2187·5 m²   (10) 0·25
3. (1) £1·68   (2) £1·97   (3) £1·77   (4) 27½p
   (5) £36·94
4. (1) 60p   (2) £100·17   (3) 21p   (4) 1·67p
   (5) £2·71½
5. (1) £15   (2) £31·50   (3) £91·89   (4) £57·37
   (5) £5·55

EXERCISE 38, page 153

1. 25   2. 11$\frac{1}{9}$ 3. 5
4. 1$\frac{1}{4}$ 5. 20   6. 50
7. 4   8. 75   9. 15
10. 6$\frac{2}{3}$ 11. 5   12. 7·14
13. 12$\frac{1}{2}$ 14. 40   15. 11$\frac{1}{9}$
16. 200

EXERCISE 39, page 155

1. 21·8%
2. 52$\frac{1}{12}$% of girls; 47$\frac{11}{12}$% of boys
3. 95% (actually 94$\frac{73}{74}$)
4. 3·82
5. £33·90
6. £1·30
7. £2·32½
8. 0·84 kg, 0·168 kg, 0·112 kg
9. First partner received £333; second partner £270; third partner £207
10. 390 g

11. 53%
12. 97·95%
13. 18$\frac{2}{11}$%
14. £127·53
15. 20·1%; 16%; 24·5%; 5·5%
16. $\begin{cases} \text{Sum that must be insured} = £3245\cdot51 \\ \text{Premium} \qquad\qquad\qquad = £153\cdot53 \end{cases}$
17. £48·19
18. 13·84%
19. 23·87%

Exercise 40, page 163

1. 44 m²   2. 1098 m²   3. 5·25 m²
4. 0·316 km²   5. 24 m   6. 126 m
7. £5·84   8. 140·96 m²   9. 22·44 m²
10. 22p   11. £17·85   12. £55
13. (1) 6000 francs   (2) £461·54
14. 218 750 m²   15. 1·764 m²   16. 2·1888 m²
17. 5472 m² of forest

Exercise 41, page 167

1. 231 kl   2. 46 875 m³   3. 2·403 MN
4. £1920   5. 4·167 m   6. 8 Ml/min
7. 7 × 10⁷ mm³   8. $\frac{1}{12}$ mm   9. 12·5 m
10. 2 m   11. 486 t   12. 25·92 t

Exercise 42, page 175

1. 437 m²; 16·58   2. 14·85 m²   3. 23 120 m³
4. 542·2 m²; 108·3 m (if E is a point due south of A and due east of D, AED is a right-angled triangle with two equal sides. Thus AE (=ED) can be found by Pythagoras' Theorem.)
5. 706·86 m²   6. Nearly 293$\frac{3}{4}$ m   7. 19 920 mm³
8. 6·82 g   9. 1·90 t   10. 103·6 m³
11. 21 950 mm² (approx.)   12. 26 000 mm³ (approx.)

Exercise 43, page 181

1. £46·75   2. £7·42, £44·52   3. £220·05
4. £39·17   5. £325·64   6. £60·80
7. £6·70   8. £207·87   9. £8·54
10. £133·89; £2024·39   11. 4$\frac{1}{2}$ years
12. £750   13. 4$\frac{1}{2}$%   14. £110
15. 2$\frac{1}{2}$%   16. 15%   17. £756

EXERCISE 44, page 185

1. £20·20   2. £48·05   3. £43·71
4. £34·42   5. £325·22   6. £422·30
7. £298·31   8. £1350·87½   9. £118
10. (1) £325·27   (2) £30·03   11. £352·65
12. £268·23   13. £356·91
14. (a) 686·38   (b) £919·81

EXERCISE 45, page 188

1. 20%   2. £1·29½ per 100   3. 12·71%
4. 24p   5. 7p loss   6. 79·3%
7. 11·06%   8. 27·75%; 14·05%; 17·47%

LOGARITHMS

	0	1	2	3	4	5	6	7	8	9	1	2	3	4	5	6	7	8	9
10	0000	0043	0086	0128	0170	0212	0253	0294	0334	0374	4	8	12	17	21	25	29	33	3
11	0414	0453	0492	0531	0569	0607	0645	0682	0719	0755	4	8	11	15	19	23	26	30	3
12	0792	0828	0864	0899	0934	0969	1004	1038	1072	1106	3	7	10	14	17	21	24	28	3
13	1139	1173	1206	1239	1271	1303	1335	1367	1399	1430	3	6	10	13	16	19	23	26	2
14	1461	1492	1523	1553	1584	1614	1644	1673	1703	1732	3	6	9	12	15	18	21	24	2
15	1761	1790	1818	1847	1875	1903	1931	1959	1987	2014	3	6	8	11	14	17	20	22	2
16	2041	2068	2095	2122	2148	2175	2201	2227	2253	2279	3	5	8	11	13	16	18	21	2
17	2304	2330	2355	2380	2405	2430	2455	2480	2504	2529	2	5	7	10	12	15	17	20	2
18	2553	2577	2601	2625	2648	2672	2695	2718	2742	2765	2	5	7	9	12	14	16	19	2
19	2788	2810	2833	2856	2878	2900	2923	2945	2967	2989	2	4	7	9	11	13	16	18	2
20	3010	3032	3054	3075	3096	3118	3139	3160	3181	3201	2	4	6	8	11	13	15	17	1
21	3222	3243	3263	3284	3304	3324	3345	3365	3385	3404	2	4	6	8	10	12	14	16	1
22	3424	3444	3464	3483	3502	3522	3541	3560	3579	3598	2	4	6	8	10	12	14	15	1
23	3617	3636	3655	3674	3692	3711	3729	3747	3766	3784	2	4	6	7	9	11	13	15	1
24	3802	3820	3838	3856	3874	3892	3909	3927	3945	3962	2	4	5	7	9	11	12	14	1
25	3979	3997	4014	4031	4048	4065	4082	4099	4116	4133	2	3	5	7	9	10	12	14	1
26	4150	4166	4183	4200	4216	4232	4249	4265	4281	4298	2	3	5	7	8	10	11	13	1
27	4314	4330	4346	4362	4378	4393	4409	4425	4440	4456	2	3	5	6	8	9	11	13	1
28	4472	4487	4502	4518	4533	4548	4564	4579	4594	4609	2	3	5	6	8	9	11	12	1
29	4624	4639	4654	4669	4683	4698	4713	4728	4742	4757	1	3	4	6	7	9	10	12	1
30	4771	4786	4800	4814	4829	4843	4857	4871	4886	4900	1	3	4	6	7	9	10	11	1
31	4914	4928	4942	4955	4969	4983	4997	5011	5024	5038	1	3	4	5	7	8	10	11	1
32	5051	5065	5079	5092	5105	5119	5132	5145	5159	5172	1	3	4	5	7	8	9	11	1
33	5185	5198	5211	5224	5237	5250	5263	5276	5289	5302	1	3	4	5	6	8	9	10	1
34	5315	5328	5340	5353	5366	5378	5391	5403	5416	5428	1	3	4	5	6	8	9	10	1
35	5441	5453	5465	5478	5490	5502	5514	5527	5539	5551	1	2	4	5	6	7	9	10	1
36	5563	5575	5587	5599	5611	5623	5635	5647	5658	5670	1	2	4	5	6	7	8	10	1
37	5682	5694	5705	5717	5729	5740	5752	5763	5775	5786	1	2	3	5	6	7	8	9	1
38	5798	5809	5821	5832	5843	5855	5866	5877	5888	5899	1	2	3	5	6	7	8	9	1
39	5911	5922	5933	5944	5955	5966	5977	5988	5999	6010	1	2	3	4	5	7	8	9	1
40	6021	6031	6042	6053	6064	6075	6085	6096	6107	6117	1	2	3	4	5	6	7	9	1
41	6128	6138	6149	6160	6170	6180	6191	6201	6212	6222	1	2	3	4	5	6	7	8	
42	6232	6243	6253	6263	6274	6284	6294	6304	6314	6325	1	2	3	4	5	6	7	8	
43	6335	6345	6355	6365	6375	6385	6395	6405	6415	6425	1	2	3	4	5	6	7	8	
44	6435	6444	6454	6464	6474	6484	6493	6503	6513	6522	1	2	3	4	5	6	7	8	
45	6532	6542	6551	6561	6571	6580	6590	6599	6609	6618	1	2	3	4	5	6	7	8	
46	6628	6637	6646	6656	6665	6675	6684	6693	6702	6712	1	2	3	4	5	6	7	7	
47	6721	6730	6739	6749	6758	6767	6776	6785	6794	6803	1	2	3	4	5	5	6	7	
48	6812	6821	6830	6839	6848	6857	6866	6875	6884	6893	1	2	3	4	4	5	6	7	
49	6902	6911	6920	6928	6937	6946	6955	6964	6972	6981	1	2	3	4	4	5	6	7	
50	6990	6998	7007	7016	7024	7033	7042	7050	7059	7067	1	2	3	3	4	5	6	7	
51	7076	7084	7093	7101	7110	7118	7126	7135	7143	7152	1	2	3	3	4	5	6	7	
52	7160	7168	7177	7185	7193	7202	7210	7218	7226	7235	1	2	2	3	4	5	6	7	
53	7243	7251	7259	7267	7275	7284	7292	7300	7308	7316	1	2	2	3	4	5	6	6	
54	7324	7332	7340	7348	7356	7364	7372	7380	7388	7396	1	2	2	3	4	5	6	6	
	0	1	2	3	4	5	6	7	8	9	1	2	3	4	5	6	7	8	9

LOGARITHMS

	0	1	2	3	4	5	6	7	8	9	1	2	3	4	5	6	7	8	9
55	7404	7412	7419	7427	7435	7443	7451	7459	7466	7474	1	2	2	3	4	5	5	6	7
56	7482	7490	7497	7505	7513	7520	7528	7536	7543	7551	1	2	2	3	4	5	5	6	7
57	7559	7566	7574	7582	7589	7597	7604	7612	7619	7627	1	2	2	3	4	5	5	6	7
58	7634	7642	7649	7657	7664	7672	7679	7686	7694	7701	1	1	2	3	4	4	5	6	7
59	7709	7716	7723	7731	7738	7745	7752	7760	7767	7774	1	1	2	3	4	4	5	6	7
60	7782	7789	7796	7803	7810	7818	7825	7832	7839	7846	1	1	2	3	4	4	5	6	6
61	7853	7860	7868	7875	7882	7889	7896	7903	7910	7917	1	1	2	3	4	4	5	6	6
62	7924	7931	7938	7945	7952	7959	7966	7973	7980	7987	1	1	2	3	3	4	5	6	6
63	7993	8000	8007	8014	8021	8028	8035	8041	8048	8055	1	1	2	3	3	4	5	6	6
64	8062	8069	8075	8082	8089	8096	8102	8109	8116	8122	1	1	2	3	3	4	5	5	6
65	8129	8136	8142	8149	8156	8162	8169	8176	8182	8189	1	1	2	3	3	4	5	5	6
66	8195	8202	8209	8215	8222	8228	8235	8241	8248	8254	1	1	2	3	3	4	5	5	6
67	8261	8267	8274	8280	8287	8293	8299	8306	8312	8319	1	1	2	3	3	4	4	5	6
68	8325	8331	8338	8344	8351	8357	8363	8370	8376	8382	1	1	2	3	3	4	4	5	6
69	8388	8395	8401	8407	8414	8420	8426	8432	8439	8445	1	1	2	3	3	4	4	5	6
70	8451	8457	8463	8470	8476	8482	8488	8494	8500	8506	1	1	2	2	3	4	4	5	6
71	8513	8519	8525	8531	8537	8543	8549	8555	8561	8567	1	1	2	2	3	4	4	5	5
72	8573	8579	8585	8591	8597	8603	8609	8615	8621	8627	1	1	2	2	3	4	4	5	5
73	8633	8639	8645	8651	8657	8663	8669	8675	8681	8686	1	1	2	2	3	4	4	5	5
74	8692	8698	8704	8710	8716	8722	8727	8733	8739	8745	1	1	2	2	3	4	4	5	5
75	8751	8756	8762	8768	8774	8779	8785	8791	8797	8802	1	1	2	2	3	3	4	5	5
76	8808	8814	8820	8825	8831	8837	8842	8848	8854	8859	1	1	2	2	3	3	4	5	5
77	8865	8871	8876	8882	8887	8893	8899	8904	8910	8915	1	1	2	2	3	3	4	4	5
78	8921	8927	8932	8938	8943	8949	8954	8960	8965	8971	1	1	2	2	3	3	4	4	5
79	8976	8982	8987	8993	8998	9004	9009	9015	9020	9025	1	1	2	2	3	3	4	4	5
80	9031	9036	9042	9047	9053	9058	9063	9069	9074	9079	1	1	2	2	3	3	4	4	5
81	9085	9090	9096	9101	9106	9112	9117	9122	9128	9133	1	1	2	2	3	3	4	4	5
82	9138	9143	9149	9154	9159	9165	9170	9175	9180	9186	1	1	2	2	3	3	4	4	5
83	9191	9196	9201	9206	9212	9217	9222	9227	9232	9238	1	1	2	2	3	3	4	4	5
84	9243	9248	9253	9258	9263	9269	9274	9279	9284	9289	1	1	2	2	3	3	4	4	5
85	9294	9299	9304	9309	9315	9320	9325	9330	9335	9340	1	1	2	2	3	3	4	4	5
86	9345	9350	9355	9360	9365	9370	9375	9380	9385	9390	1	1	2	2	3	3	4	4	5
87	9395	9400	9405	9410	9415	9420	9425	9430	9435	9440	0	1	1	2	2	3	3	4	4
88	9445	9450	9455	9460	9465	9469	9474	9479	9484	9489	0	1	1	2	2	3	3	4	4
89	9494	9499	9504	9509	9513	9518	9523	9528	9533	9538	0	1	1	2	2	3	3	4	4
90	9542	9547	9552	9557	9562	9566	9571	9576	9581	9586	0	1	1	2	2	3	3	4	4
91	9590	9595	9600	9605	9609	9614	9619	9624	9628	9633	0	1	1	2	2	3	3	4	4
92	9638	9643	9647	9652	9657	9661	9666	9671	9675	9680	0	1	1	2	2	3	3	4	4
93	9685	9689	9694	9699	9703	9708	9713	9717	9722	9727	0	1	1	2	2	3	3	4	4
94	9731	9736	9741	9745	9750	9754	9759	9764	9768	9773	0	1	1	2	2	3	3	4	4
95	9777	9782	9786	9791	9795	9800	9805	9809	9814	9818	0	1	1	2	2	3	3	4	4
96	9823	9827	9832	9836	9841	9845	9850	9854	9859	9863	0	1	1	2	2	3	3	4	4
97	9868	9872	9877	9881	9886	9890	9894	9899	9903	9908	0	1	1	2	2	3	3	4	4
98	9912	9917	9921	9926	9930	9934	9939	9943	9948	9952	0	1	1	2	2	3	3	4	4
99	9956	9961	9965	9969	9974	9978	9983	9987	9991	9996	0	1	1	2	2	3	3	4	4
	0	1	2	3	4	5	6	7	8	9	1	2	3	4	5	6	7	8	9

ANTI-LOGARITHMS

	0	1	2	3	4	5	6	7	8	9	1	2	3	4	5	6	7	8
·00	1000	1002	1005	1007	1009	1012	1014	1016	1019	1021	0	0	1	1	1	1	2	2
·01	1023	1026	1028	1030	1033	1035	1038	1040	1042	1045	0	0	1	1	1	1	2	2
·02	1047	1050	1052	1054	1057	1059	1062	1064	1067	1069	0	0	1	1	1	1	2	2
·03	1072	1074	1076	1079	1081	1084	1086	1089	1091	1094	0	0	1	1	1	1	2	2
·04	1096	1099	1102	1104	1107	1109	1112	1114	1117	1119	0	1	1	1	1	2	2	2
·05	1122	1125	1127	1130	1132	1135	1138	1140	1143	1146	0	1	1	1	1	2	2	2
·06	1148	1151	1153	1156	1159	1161	1164	1167	1169	1172	0	1	1	1	1	2	2	2
·07	1175	1178	1180	1183	1186	1189	1191	1194	1197	1199	0	1	1	1	1	2	2	2
·08	1202	1205	1208	1211	1213	1216	1219	1222	1225	1227	0	1	1	1	1	2	2	2
·09	1230	1233	1236	1239	1242	1245	1247	1250	1253	1256	0	1	1	1	1	2	2	2
·10	1259	1262	1265	1268	1271	1274	1276	1279	1282	1285	0	1	1	1	1	2	2	2
·11	1288	1291	1294	1297	1300	1303	1306	1309	1312	1315	0	1	1	1	2	2	2	2
·12	1318	1321	1324	1327	1330	1334	1337	1340	1343	1346	0	1	1	1	2	2	2	2
·13	1349	1352	1355	1358	1361	1365	1368	1371	1374	1377	0	1	1	1	2	2	2	2
·14	1380	1384	1387	1390	1393	1396	1400	1403	1406	1409	0	1	1	1	2	2	2	3
·15	1413	1416	1419	1422	1426	1429	1432	1435	1439	1442	0	1	1	1	2	2	2	3
·16	1445	1449	1452	1455	1459	1462	1466	1469	1472	1476	0	1	1	1	2	2	2	3
·17	1479	1483	1486	1489	1493	1496	1500	1503	1507	1510	0	1	1	1	2	2	2	3
·18	1514	1517	1521	1524	1528	1531	1535	1538	1542	1545	0	1	1	1	2	2	2	3
·19	1549	1552	1556	1560	1563	1567	1570	1574	1578	1581	0	1	1	1	2	2	3	3
·20	1585	1589	1592	1596	1600	1603	1607	1611	1614	1618	0	1	1	1	2	2	3	3
·21	1622	1626	1629	1633	1637	1641	1644	1648	1652	1656	0	1	1	2	2	2	3	3
·22	1660	1663	1667	1671	1675	1679	1683	1687	1690	1694	0	1	1	2	2	2	3	3
·23	1698	1702	1706	1710	1714	1718	1722	1726	1730	1734	0	1	1	2	2	2	3	3
·24	1738	1742	1746	1750	1754	1758	1762	1766	1770	1774	0	1	1	2	2	2	3	3
·25	1778	1782	1786	1791	1795	1799	1803	1807	1811	1816	0	1	1	2	2	3	3	3
·26	1820	1824	1828	1832	1837	1841	1845	1849	1854	1858	0	1	1	2	2	3	3	3
·27	1862	1866	1871	1875	1879	1884	1888	1892	1897	1901	0	1	1	2	2	3	3	3
·28	1905	1910	1914	1919	1923	1928	1932	1936	1941	1945	0	1	1	2	2	3	3	4
·29	1950	1954	1959	1963	1968	1972	1977	1982	1986	1991	0	1	1	2	2	3	3	4
·30	1995	2000	2004	2009	2014	2018	2023	2028	2032	2037	0	1	1	2	2	3	3	4
·31	2042	2046	2051	2056	2061	2065	2070	2075	2080	2084	0	1	1	2	2	3	3	4
·32	2089	2094	2099	2104	2109	2113	2118	2123	2128	2133	0	1	1	2	2	3	3	4
·33	2138	2143	2148	2153	2158	2163	2168	2173	2178	2183	0	1	1	2	2	3	3	4
·34	2188	2193	2198	2203	2208	2213	2218	2223	2228	2234	1	1	2	2	3	3	4	4
·35	2239	2244	2249	2254	2259	2265	2270	2275	2280	2286	1	1	2	2	3	3	4	4
·36	2291	2296	2301	2307	2312	2317	2323	2328	2333	2339	1	1	2	2	3	3	4	4
·37	2344	2350	2355	2360	2366	2371	2377	2382	2388	2393	1	1	2	2	3	3	4	4
·38	2399	2404	2410	2415	2421	2427	2432	2438	2443	2449	1	1	2	2	3	3	4	4
·39	2455	2460	2466	2472	2477	2483	2489	2495	2500	2506	1	1	2	2	3	3	4	5
·40	2512	2518	2523	2529	2535	2541	2547	2553	2559	2564	1	1	2	2	3	3	4	5
·41	2570	2576	2582	2588	2594	2600	2606	2612	2618	2624	1	1	2	2	3	4	4	5
·42	2630	2636	2642	2648	2655	2661	2667	2673	2679	2685	1	1	2	2	3	4	4	5
·43	2692	2698	2704	2710	2716	2723	2729	2735	2742	2748	1	1	2	2	3	4	4	5
·44	2754	2761	2767	2773	2780	2786	2793	2799	2805	2812	1	1	2	3	3	4	4	5
·45	2818	2825	2831	2838	2844	2851	2858	2864	2871	2877	1	1	2	3	3	4	5	5
·46	2884	2891	2897	2904	2911	2917	2924	2931	2938	2944	1	1	2	3	3	4	5	5
·47	2951	2958	2965	2972	2979	2985	2992	2999	3006	3013	1	1	2	3	3	4	5	6
·48	3020	3027	3034	3041	3048	3055	3062	3069	3076	3083	1	1	2	3	4	4	5	6
·49	3090	3097	3105	3112	3119	3126	3133	3141	3148	3155	1	1	2	3	4	4	5	6
	0	1	2	3	4	5	6	7	8	9	1	2	3	4	5	6	7	8	9

ANTI-LOGARITHMS

	0	1	2	3	4	5	6	7	8	9	1	2	3	4	5	6	7	8	9
·50	3162	3170	3177	3184	3192	3199	3206	3214	3221	3228	1	1	2	3	4	4	5	6	7
·51	3236	3243	3251	3258	3266	3273	3281	3289	3296	3304	1	2	2	3	4	5	5	6	7
·52	3311	3319	3327	3334	3342	3350	3357	3365	3373	3381	1	2	2	3	4	5	5	6	7
·53	3388	3396	3404	3412	3420	3428	3436	3443	3451	3459	1	2	2	3	4	5	6	6	7
·54	3467	3475	3483	3491	3499	3508	3516	3524	3532	3540	1	2	2	3	4	5	6	6	7
·55	3548	3556	3565	3573	3581	3589	3597	3606	3614	3622	1	2	2	3	4	5	6	7	7
·56	3631	3639	3648	3656	3664	3673	3681	3690	3698	3707	1	2	3	3	4	5	6	7	8
·57	3715	3724	3733	3741	3750	3758	3767	3776	3784	3793	1	2	3	3	4	5	6	7	8
·58	3802	3811	3819	3828	3837	3846	3855	3864	3873	3882	1	2	3	4	4	5	6	7	8
·59	3890	3899	3908	3917	3926	3936	3945	3954	3963	3972	1	2	3	4	5	5	6	7	8
·60	3981	3990	3999	4009	4018	4027	4036	4046	4055	4064	1	2	3	4	5	6	7	7	8
·61	4074	4083	4093	4102	4111	4121	4130	4140	4150	4159	1	2	3	4	5	6	7	8	9
·62	4169	4178	4188	4198	4207	4217	4227	4236	4246	4256	1	2	3	4	5	6	7	8	9
·63	4266	4276	4285	4295	4305	4315	4325	4335	4345	4355	1	2	3	4	5	6	7	8	9
·64	4365	4375	4385	4395	4406	4416	4426	4436	4446	4457	1	2	3	4	5	6	7	8	9
·65	4467	4477	4487	4498	4508	4519	4529	4539	4550	4560	1	2	3	4	5	6	7	8	9
·66	4571	4581	4592	4603	4613	4624	4634	4645	4656	4667	1	2	3	4	5	6	7	8	10
·67	4677	4688	4699	4710	4721	4732	4742	4753	4764	4775	1	2	3	4	5	7	8	9	10
·68	4786	4797	4808	4819	4831	4842	4853	4864	4875	4887	1	2	3	4	6	7	8	9	10
·69	4898	4909	4920	4932	4943	4955	4966	4977	4989	5000	1	2	3	5	6	7	8	9	10
·70	5012	5023	5035	5047	5058	5070	5082	5093	5105	5117	1	2	4	5	6	7	8	9	11
·71	5129	5140	5152	5164	5176	5188	5200	5212	5224	5236	1	2	4	5	6	7	8	10	11
·72	5248	5260	5272	5284	5297	5309	5321	5333	5346	5358	1	2	4	5	6	7	9	10	11
·73	5370	5383	5395	5408	5420	5433	5445	5458	5470	5483	1	3	4	5	6	8	9	10	11
·74	5495	5508	5521	5534	5546	5559	5572	5585	5598	5610	1	3	4	5	6	8	9	10	12
·75	5623	5636	5649	5662	5675	5689	5702	5715	5728	5741	1	3	4	5	7	8	9	10	12
·76	5754	5768	5781	5794	5808	5821	5834	5848	5861	5875	1	3	4	5	7	8	9	11	12
·77	5888	5902	5916	5929	5943	5957	5970	5984	5998	6012	1	3	4	6	7	8	10	11	12
·78	6026	6039	6053	6067	6081	6095	6109	6124	6138	6152	1	3	4	6	7	8	10	11	13
·79	6166	6180	6194	6209	6223	6237	6252	6266	6281	6295	1	3	4	6	7	9	10	12	13
·80	6310	6324	6339	6353	6368	6383	6397	6412	6427	6442	1	3	4	6	7	9	10	12	13
·81	6457	6471	6486	6501	6516	6531	6546	6561	6577	6592	2	3	5	6	8	9	11	12	14
·82	6607	6622	6637	6653	6668	6683	6699	6714	6730	6745	2	3	5	6	8	9	11	12	14
·83	6761	6776	6792	6808	6823	6839	6855	6871	6887	6902	2	3	5	6	8	9	11	13	14
·84	6918	6934	6950	6966	6982	6998	7015	7031	7047	7063	2	3	5	6	8	10	11	13	14
·85	7079	7096	7112	7129	7145	7161	7178	7194	7211	7228	2	3	5	7	8	10	12	13	15
·86	7244	7261	7278	7295	7311	7328	7345	7362	7379	7396	2	3	5	7	8	10	12	14	15
·87	7413	7430	7447	7464	7482	7499	7516	7534	7551	7568	2	3	5	7	9	10	12	14	16
·88	7586	7603	7621	7638	7656	7674	7691	7709	7727	7745	2	4	5	7	9	11	12	14	16
·89	7762	7780	7798	7816	7834	7852	7870	7889	7907	7925	2	4	5	7	9	11	13	14	16
·90	7943	7962	7980	7998	8017	8035	8054	8072	8091	8110	2	4	6	7	9	11	13	15	17
·91	8128	8147	8166	8185	8204	8222	8241	8260	8279	8299	2	4	6	8	10	11	13	15	17
·92	8318	8337	8356	8375	8395	8414	8433	8453	8472	8492	2	4	6	8	10	12	14	15	17
·93	8511	8531	8551	8570	8590	8610	8630	8650	8670	8690	2	4	6	8	10	12	14	16	18
·94	8710	8730	8750	8770	8790	8810	8831	8851	8872	8892	2	4	6	8	10	12	14	16	18
·95	8913	8933	8954	8974	8995	9016	9036	9057	9078	9099	2	4	6	8	10	12	14	17	19
·96	9120	9141	9162	9183	9204	9226	9247	9268	9290	9311	2	4	6	8	11	13	15	17	19
·97	9333	9354	9376	9397	9419	9441	9462	9484	9506	9528	2	4	7	9	11	13	15	17	20
·98	9550	9572	9594	9616	9638	9661	9683	9705	9727	9750	2	4	7	9	11	13	16	18	20
·99	9772	9795	9817	9840	9863	9886	9908	9931	9954	9977	2	5	7	9	11	14	16	18	21
	0	1	2	3	4	5	6	7	8	9	1	2	3	4	5	6	7	8	9

TEACH YOURSELF BOOKS

MATHEMATICS, SCIENCE AND TECHNICAL

05689 4	**Plumbing**		60p
	J. H. Innes		
05701 7	**Radio Servicing**		50p
	L. Butterworth		
12494 6	**Seamanship**		50p
	T. F. Wickham & N. Hefford		
15368 7	**Slide Rule**		40p
	B. Snodgrass		
05727 0	**Statistics**		50p
	R. Goodman		
05738 6	**Trigonometry**		40p
	P. Abbott		
10983 3	**The Weather**		60p
	Sir Graham Sutton		
15247 8	**Welding**		50p
	C. Bainbrigde		
05748 3	**Zoology**		50p
	T. M. Savory		

All these books are available at your bookshop or news-agent, or can be ordered direct from the publisher: Teach Yourself Books, P.O. Box 11, Falmouth, Cornwall

Please send cheque or postal order. No currency, and allow the following for postage and packing:

UK AND EIRE—15p for the first book plus 5p per copy for each additional book ordered to a maximum charge of 50p.

OVERSEAS CUSTOMERS AND B.F.P.O.—please allow 20p for the first book and 10p per copy for each additional book.

While every effort is made to keep prices low, it is some-times necessary to increase prices at short notice. Teach Yourself Books reserve the right to show new retail prices on covers which may differ from those previously advertised in the text or elsewhere.